London • Frankfurt am Main • Leipzig • New York

The New
Anthology
of Music

Edited by Julia Winterson

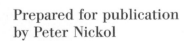

Prepared for publication
by Peter Nickol

Edexcel
Success through qualifications

Peters Edition Limited
Hinrichsen House
10–12 Baches Street
London
N1 6DN

Tel: 020 7553 4000
Fax: 020 7490 4921
email: sales@uk.edition-peters.com
internet: www.edition-peters.com

First published 2000
Reprinted 2000 (twice), 2001, 2002, 2003, 2004
© 2000 by Hinrichsen Edition, Peters Edition Limited, London

ISBN 1 901507 03 3

Companion 4-CD Set available EP 7591CD
ISBN 1 901507 04 1

A catalogue record for this book is
available from the British Library

Cover design by Adam Hay Design
Music engraving by Global Music Service, www.globalmusicservice.com
Printed by Caligraving Limited, Thetford, Norfolk, England

Foreword

The New Anthology of Music is a collection of 63 pieces of music each with a recording and a transcription. It has been designed to accompany the Edexcel Advanced Subsidiary and Advanced GCE in Music but it will also be a useful resource for GCSE teachers and anyone who wishes to learn more about music. The pieces have been grouped according to genre, and cover nine Areas of Study:

- Music for Large Ensemble
- Twentieth-Century Art Music
- Music for Small Ensemble
- Keyboard Music
- Sacred Vocal Music
- Secular Vocal Music
- Music for Film and Television
- Popular Music and Jazz
- World Music

With the exception of the Beatles' *A Day in the Life* (for copyright reasons), the four Anthology CDs contain a recording of each piece.

An important aim in selecting the 63 pieces was to reveal the breadth of music's expressive possibilities and to find works that could illustrate a multiplicity of musical elements, formal characteristics, resources, and social and cultural contexts. As with any anthology there are limits to how far the selection can be representative. The chosen works are not intended to offer a comprehensive collection of music (nor could they), nor is each work necessarily regarded as a landmark in the history of music. World music is represented for the first time, with six highly contrasted examples; but we are aware that this is no more than a small selection from a huge field.

Wherever possible the pieces are complete in themselves or are whole movements. Each piece has been transcribed in a format appropriate to the style of music; thus different styles of notation have been used. It is recognised that the use of notation is not common practice in some of the musical examples, but it was considered important nevertheless that notation be included for the purpose of analysis and to offer opportunities for performance.

The anthology contains all the music that needs to be studied for the assessment tasks of Part 2 of the units in Listening and Understanding and Analysing Music, and will be a useful listening resource for Part 1. In general the recordings on the CDs closely match the printed scores; but in a few cases, particularly with 'early' music, there are slight differences owing to performance practice, whose identification will help develop candidates' aural perception. A few recordings have been chosen to stimulate debate on matters such as authenticity in performance.

The specification encourages the integration of the various musical disciplines, and every Area of Study provides opportunities not only for study of repertoire but also for composing and performing activities. Although candidates will not be assessed on their performance of pieces in the anthology, they may enjoy playing some of the transcriptions. Such music-making should be particularly valuable in backing up historical and analytical studies.

The anthology includes pieces which use some of the composition techniques found in Units 2 and 5 of the Edexcel Specification. There is no requirement to link composition topics with Areas of Study, but there is much within these pages to enthuse and help direct the steps of all aspiring composers.

Julia Winterson

Contents

Music for Large Ensemble   *Page*

1 J. S. Bach .... Brandenburg Concerto No. 4 in G: movement I 7

2 Haydn .... Symphony No 26 in D minor, 'Lamentatione': movement I 31

3 Berlioz .... Harold in Italy: movement III 42

4 Wagner .... Prelude *to* Tristan und Isolde 65

5 Debussy .... Prélude à l'après-midi d'un faune 86

6 Tippett .... Concerto for Double String Orchestra: movement I 120

20th-Century Art Music

7 Stravinsky .... Pulcinella Suite: Sinfonia, Gavotta and Vivo 139

8 Webern .... Quartet Op. 22: movement I 160

9 Shostakovich .... String Quartet No. 8, Op. 110: movement I 163

10 Cage .... Sonatas and Interludes for Prepared Piano: Sonatas I–III 166

11 Berio .... Sequenza III for female voice 171

12 Reich .... New York Counterpoint: movement II 176

Music for Small Ensemble

13 Holborne .... Pavane 'The image of melancholy' and Galliard 'Ecce quam bonum' ... 191

14 G. Gabrieli .... Sonata pian' e forte 194

15 Corelli .... Trio Sonata in D, Op. 3 No. 2: movement IV 200

16 Haydn .... String Quartet in E♭, Op. 33 No. 2, 'The Joke': movement IV 202

17 Beethoven .... Septet in E♭, Op. 20: movement I 207

18 Brahms .... Piano Quintet in F minor, Op. 34: movement III 231

19 Poulenc .... Sonata for Horn, Trumpet and Trombone: movement I 242

Keyboard Music

20 Sweelinck .... Pavana Lachrimae 245

21 J. S. Bach .... Partita No. 4 in D, BWV 828: Sarabande and Gigue 249

22 Mozart .... Piano Sonata in B♭, K.333: movement I 253

23 Schumann .... Kinderscenen, Op. 15: Nos. 1, 3 and 11 258

24 Debussy .... Pour le piano: Sarabande 260

25 Shostakovich .... Prelude and Fugue in A, Op. 87 No. 7 262

Sacred Vocal Music

26 Taverner .... O Wilhelme, pastor bone 266

27 G. Gabrieli .... In ecclesiis 269

28 J. S. Bach .... Cantata No. 48, 'Ich elender Mensch': movements I–IV 288

29 Haydn .... 'Quoniam tu solus' *from* The Nelson Mass 299

30 Bruckner .... Locus iste 305

31 Stravinsky .... Symphony of Psalms: movement III 307

32 Tavener .... The Lamb 344

Secular Vocal Music

33	Dowland	Flow my tears	347
34	Weelkes	Sing we at pleasure	349
35	Monteverdi	Ohimè, se tanto amate	353
36	Purcell	'Thy hand, Belinda' and 'When I am laid in earth' *from* Dido and Aeneas	356
37	Haydn	My mother bids me bind my hair	359
38	Schubert	Der Doppelgänger	361
39	Fauré	Après un rêve	363
40	Schoenberg	'Der kranke Mond' *from* Pierrot Lunaire	364
41	Gershwin	'Summertime' *from* Porgy and Bess	366

Music for Film and Television

42	Georges Auric	Passport to Pimlico: The Siege of Burgundy	369
43	Leonard Bernstein	On the Waterfront: Symphonic Suite (opening)	374
44	Jerry Goldsmith	Planet of the Apes: The Hunt (opening)	388
45	John Williams	ET: Flying Theme	409
46	Barrington Pheloung	Morse on the Case	433
47	James Horner	Titanic: 'Take her to sea, Mr Murdoch'	440

Popular Music and Jazz

48	Louis Armstrong and his Hot Five	West End Blues	461
49	Duke Ellington and his Orchestra	Black and Tan Fantasy	465
50	Miles Davis Quintet	Four (opening)	468
51	Howlin' Wolf	I'm leavin' you	471
52	Carl Perkins	Honey don't	477
53	The Kinks	Waterloo Sunset	483
54	The Beatles	A Day in the Life	487
55	Desmond Dekker and the Aces	You can get it if you really want	496
56	Van Morrison	Tupelo Honey	501
57	Oasis	Don't look back in anger	509

World Music

58	Ram Narayan (India)	Rag Bhairav	519
59	Gong Kebyar de Sebatu (Bali)	Baris Melampahan	522
60	Red Stripe Ebony Steelband (Trinidad)	Yellow Bird	528
61	Niall Keegan (Ireland)	Tom McElvogue's (jig) and New Irish Barndance (reel)	530
62	Mustapha Tettey Addy (Ghana)	Agbekor Dance	532
63	Familia Valera Miranda (Cuba)	Se quema la chumbambá	534

Glossary of foreign terms			537
Translations of sung texts			538
Copyright acknowledgements			541
Index			543

Acknowledgements

Edexcel acknowledges its indebtedness to all those who contributed their time and expertise to the development of this anthology. For their advice and editorial skills in its compilation, Edexcel is grateful to the following: Hugh Benham (Chief Examiner for Music), David Ashforth, Bruce Cole, and Roy Wightman (Principal Examiners) and Steve Lewis (Qualifications Leader for Performing Arts).

Thanks go to Peter Nickol for his technical expertise through the period of preparation for publication.

Edexcel would like to express its gratitude to the following musicians who transcribed pieces: Andy Channing (59), Amy Dyson (62), Bart Gruson (63) Philip Honnor (50), Graham Redwood (49 and 51), Elizabeth Sharma (60), Neil Sorrell (58) and Mirian Walton (61). Edexcel is particularly grateful to Kevin Healy, who transcribed all of the following pieces: 48, 52, 53, 55, 56 and 57.

Music for Large Ensemble

1 Brandenburg Concerto No. 4 in G: movement I

Johann Sebastian Bach (1685–1750)

CD 1 track 1

14

24

2 Symphony No. 26 in D minor, 'Lamentatione': movement I

Joseph Haydn (1732–1809)

CD 1 track 2

36

3 Harold in Italy: movement III

Hector Berlioz (1803–1869)

CD 1 track 3

Serenade of a mountaineer of the Abbruzes to his Mistress.

Allegretto ♩. = 69

(♩. del Allegretto eguale a ♩. del Allegro assai precedente.)

49

54

56

61

4 Prelude *to* Tristan und Isolde

Richard Wagner (1813–1883)

CD 1 track 4

70

81

5 Prélude à l'après-midi d'un faune

CD 1 track 5

Claude Debussy (1862–1918)

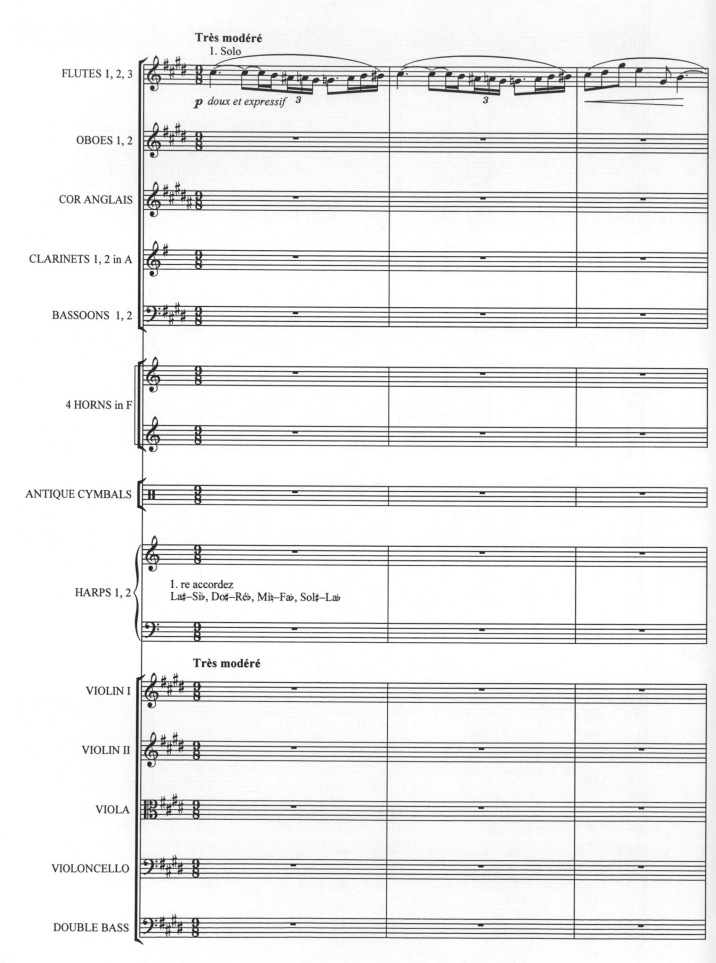

90

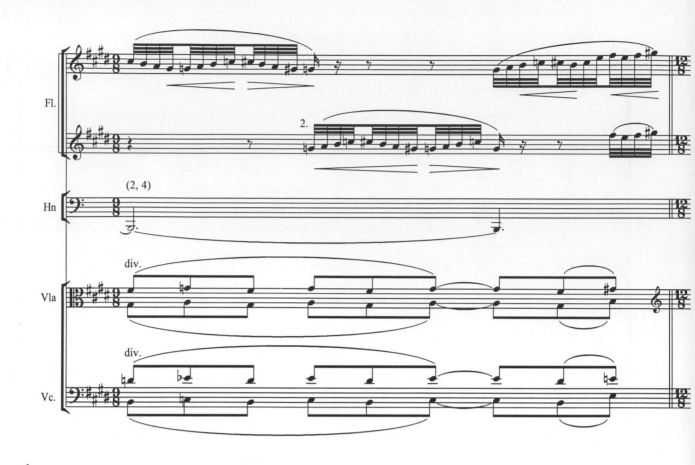

98

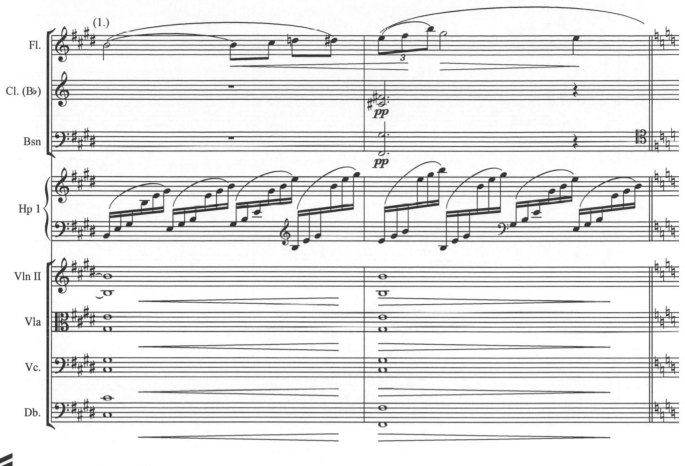

Un peu plus animé

110

accordez sur Si♯–Do♮, Ré♯–Mi♭, Fa♯–Sol♭, La♯–Si♭

114

118

6 Concerto for Double String Orchestra: movement I

Michael Tippett (1905–1998)

CD 1 track 6

Tippett writes at the head of the score: 'Unequal beats are always shown by the groupings and ligatures, which give the proper rhythms intended for that part at that time.'

* The sign ⟨ placed thus above a tie indicates that the tone is meant to be carried on to the second note which has an implied rhythmic accent, as opposed to bars 37 et simile where there is no rhythmic accent on the 5th quaver.

124

126

128

132

134

7 Pulcinella Suite: Sinfonia, Gavotta and Vivo

CD 1 tracks 7–9

Igor Stravinsky (1882–1971)
after G. B. Pergolesi (1710–1736)

I SINFONIA (Overture)

Allegro moderato ♩ = 80

139

142

144

148

VI GAVOTTA
con due variazioni

150

Variazione I

attacca

Variazione II

Allegro più tosto moderato ♩= 88

solo cantabile

accompagnando

1st time only

solo cantabile

159

8 Quartet Op. 22: movement I

CD 1 track 10

Anton Webern (1883–1945)

9 String Quartet No. 8, Op. 110: movement I

Dmitry Shostakovich (1906–1975)

CD 1 track 11

10 Sonatas and Interludes for Prepared Piano: Sonatas I–III   John Cage (1912–199

CD 1 tracks 12–14

The composer heads the score with these instructions as to how to 'prepare' the piano:

[MUTES OF VARIOUS MATERIALS ARE PLACED BETWEEN THE
STRINGS OF THE KEYS USED, THUS EFFECTING
TRANSFORMATIONS OF THE PIANO SOUNDS WITH
RESPECT TO ALL OF THEIR CHARACTERISTICS .

Table of preparations (the left TONE column is notated on a grand staff; the right TONE column gives pitch letters).

Material (1)	Strings L→R	Dist. from damper (in)	Material (2)	Strings L→R	Dist. from damper (in)	Material (3)	Strings L→R	Dist. from damper (in)	Tone
			SCREW	2-3	1 1/4 *				A
			MED. BOLT	2-3	1 3/8 *				G
			SCREW	2-3	1 5/8 *				F
			SCREW	2-3	1 13/16 *				E
			SCREW	2-3	1 3/4 *				E♭
			SM. BOLT	2-3	2 *				D
			SCREW	2-3	1 9/16 *				C♯
			FURNITURE BOLT	2-3	2 3/16 *				C
			SCREW	2-3	2 1/2 *				B
			SCREW	2-3	1 7/8 *				B♭
			MED. BOLT	2-3	2 7/8 *				A
			SCREW	2-3	2 1/4 *				A♭
			SCREW	2-3	3 3/4 *				G
			SCREW	2-3	2 5/16 *				F♯
SCREW	1-2	3/4 *	FURN. BOLT + 2 NUTS	2-3	2 7/8 *	SCREW + 2 NUTS	2-3	3 1/2 *	F
			SCREW	2-3	1 13/16 *				E
			FURNITURE BOLT	2-3	1 7/8				E♭
			SCREW	2-3	1 15/16				C♯
			SCREW	2-3	1 1/16				C
(DAMPER TO BRIDGE = 4 7/16; ADJUST ACCORDINGLY)			MED. BOLT	2-3	3 3/4				B
			SCREW	2-3	4 9/16				A
RUBBER	1-2-3	4 1/2	FURNITURE BOLT	2-3	1 1/4				G♯
			SCREW	2-3	1 3/4				F♯
			SCREW	2-3	2 5/16				F
RUBBER	1-2-3	5 3/4							E
RUBBER	1-2-3	6 1/2	FURN. BOLT + NUT	2-3	6 7/8				E♭
			FURNITURE BOLT	2-3	2 9/16				D
RUBBER	1-2-3	3 5/8							D♭
			BOLT	2-3	7 7/8				C
			BOLT	2-3	2				B
SCREW	1-2	10	SCREW	2-3	1	RUBBER	1-2-3	8 1/4	B♭
(PLASTIC (See G))	1-2-3	2 5/16				RUBBER	1-2-3	4 1/2	G♯
PLASTIC (over 1 under 2-3)	1-2-3	2 7/8				RUBBER	1-2-3	10 1/8	G
(PLASTIC (See D))	1-2-3	4 1/4				RUBBER	1-2-3	5 7/16	D♯
PLASTIC (over 1 under 2-3)	1-2-3	4 1/8				RUBBER	1-2-3	9 3/4	D
BOLT	1-2	15 1/2	BOLT	2-3	11/16	RUBBER	1-2-3	14 1/8	D♭
BOLT	1-2	14 1/2	BOLT	2-3	7/8	RUBBER	1-2-3	6 1/2	C
BOLT	1-2	14 3/4	BOLT	2-3	9/16	RUBBER	1-2-3	14	B
RUBBER	1-2-3	9 1/2	MED. BOLT	2-3	10 1/8				B♭
SCREW	1-2	5 5/8	LG. BOLT	2-3	5 5/8	SCREW + NUTS	1-2	1	A
BOLT	1-2	7 7/8	MED. BOLT	2-3	2 1/4	RUBBER	1-2-3	4 1/8	A♭
LONG BOLT	1-2	8 3/4	LG BOLT	2-3	3 1/4				G
			BOLT	2-3	11/16				D
SCREW + RUBBER	1-2	4 7/16							D
ERASER (over D, under C♯ + E♭) AM. PENCIL CO. #346	1	6 3/4							D

* MEASURE FROM BRIDGE.

SONATA I

SONATA II

Accidentals in these pieces apply only to the note they directly precede.

CD 1 track 15

Composer's Note

The performer (a singer, an actor or both) appears on stage already muttering as though pursuing an off-stage thought. She stops muttering when the applause of the public is subsiding; she resumes after a short silence (at about the 11″ of the score). The vocal actions must be timed with reference to the 10″ divisions of each page.

● = sung tones

o = whispered, unvoiced sounds

} to be held to next sound or to ⌐, ⌙

♦, φ = sung and whispered sounds as short as possible

⫴⫴⫴ , ⫴⫴⫴ , ⫴⫴⫴ , ⫴⫴⫴ = different speeds of periodically articulated sounds

⫴⫴⫴ = can be performed as fast as possible

⫴⫴⫴ = as fused and continuous as possible

ↄ , ⫴ etc. = all grace notes as fast as possible

Although the borderline between **speaking** and **singing** voice will often be blurred in actual performance, the vocal actions written on one line (a) are 'spoken' while those written on three or five lines are 'sung'. On three lines, only relative register positions are given (b); dotted lines connect notes of exactly the same pitch (c). On five lines (d) precise intervals are given, but their pitch is not absolute: each sequence of intervals (between 'spoken' sections) can be transposed to fit the vocal range of the performer; dotted lines indicate that the change of vocal colors on the same pitch must occur smoothly and without accents (e).

= intonation contour

The text is written in different ways:

(1) Sounds or groups of sounds phonetically notated:
   [a], [ka], [u], [i], [o], [ø], [ait], [be], [e], [ɛ], etc.

(2) Sounds or groups of sounds as pronounced in context:
   /gi/ as in /give/, /wo/ as in woman, /tho/ as in without, /co/ as in comes, etc.

(3) Words conventionally written and uttered:
   'give me a few words', etc.

Sounds and words lined up in parenthesis as $\left(\!/\,{}^{a}_{tru}\!/\,\right)$ must be repeated quickly in a random and slightly discontinuous way.

Groups of sounds and words in parenthesis as (to me...), (be/lo/...), (/co//ta/...), etc. must be repeated quickly in a regular way. At 15″ of the score, for instance, (to me...) to is equivalent to to me to me to; at 30″ ([e] [a]...) [a] is equivalent to [e] [a] [e] [a] [e] [a]; at 1′ the group (ta/[ka] be...) must be repeated as many times as possible for about 2″.

ʟ.	Laughter must always be clearly articulated on a wide register.
[ʔ]	= burst of laughter to be used with any vowel freely chosen
⊕	= mouth clicks
⌀	= cough
⨄	= snapping fingers gently
+	= with mouth closed
o, o—	= breathy tone, almost whispered
←o-	= breathing in, gasping
≋	= tremolo
ᵈ≋	= dental tremolo (or jaw quivering)
～ᵡ	= trilling the tongue against the upper lip (action concealed by one hand)
╫≋	= tapping very rapidly with one hand (or fingers) against the mouth (action concealed by other hand)
(hm)	= hand (or hands) over mouth
(hm)ᵚ	= moving hand cupped over mouth to affect sound (like a mute)
(hd)	= hands down

Hand, facial and bodily gestures besides those specified in the score are to be employed at the discretion of the performer according to the indicated patterns of emotions and vocal behavior (**tense**, **urgent**, **distant**, **dreamy**, etc.). The performer, however, must not try to represent or pantomime tension, urgency, distance or dreaminess but must let these cues act as a spontaneous conditioning factor to her vocal action (mainly the colour, stress and intonation aspects) and body attitudes. The processes involved in this conditioning are not assumed to be conventionalized; they must be experimented with by the performer herself according to her own emotional code, her vocal flexibility and her 'dramaturgy'.

Text by Markus Kutter:

give me	a few words	for a woman
to sing	a truth	allowing us
to build a house	without worrying	before night comes

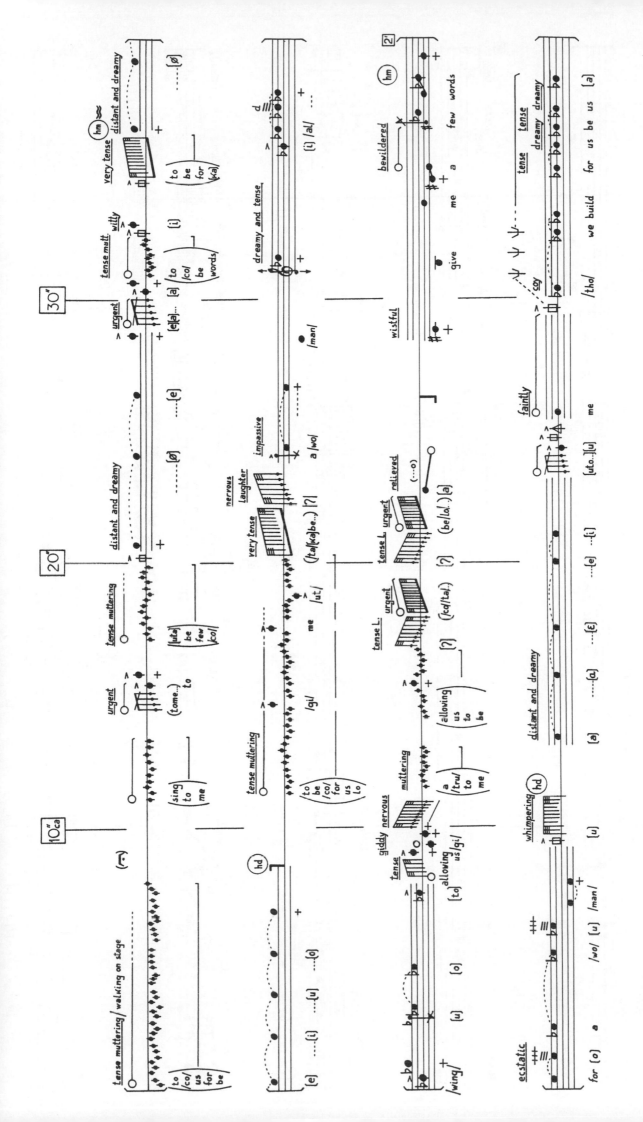

173

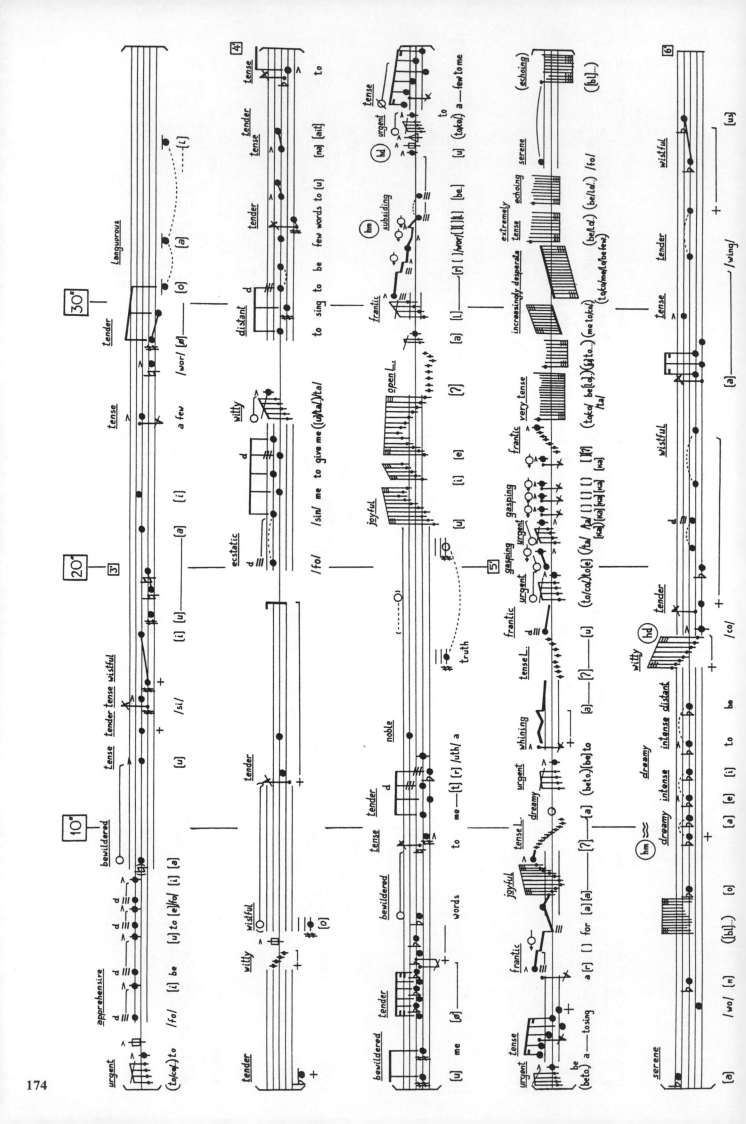

174

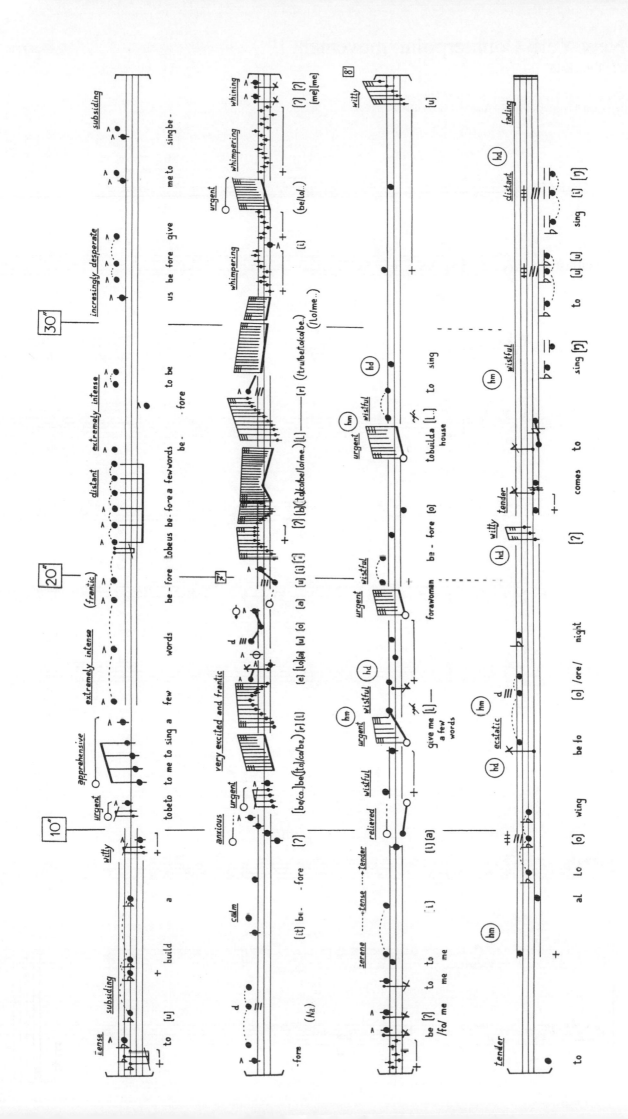

175

12 New York Counterpoint: movement II

Steve Reich (b. 1936)

The soloist pre-records eight clarinet and two bass clarinet
parts and then plays a final 11th part live against the tape.

177

184

13 Pavane 'The image of melancholy' and Galliard 'Ecce quam bonum'

Anthony Holborne (?–1602)

CD 2 tracks 1–2

The original title page of Holborne's collection reads: 'Pavans, galliards, almains and other short aeirs both grave, and light, in five parts, for viols, violins, or other musicall winde instruments'. A modern key signature has been inserted, and barlines and note-lengths regularised. More familiar modern clefs have been substituted for Holborne's originals. On the accompanying CD this pavane and galliard are performed on viols. The pitch is slightly lower than modern concert pitch.

PADUANA : The image of melancholy

GALLIARD : Ecce quam bonum

14 Sonata pian' e forte

CD 2 track 3

Giovanni Gabrieli (*c.*1555–1612)

Time signatures have been inserted. The 'violin' in Gabrieli's score was lower pitched than the modern
violin, closer to a viola in range. The performers on the accompanying CD add ornaments at various points.

195

15 Trio Sonata in D, Op. 3 No. 2: movement IV

CD 2 track 4

Arcangelo Corelli (1653–1713)

16 String Quartet in E♭, Op. 33 No. 2, 'The Joke': movement IV

Joseph Haydn (1732–1809)

CD 2 track 5

Fine

17 Septet in E♭, Op. 20: movement I

Ludwig van Beethoven (1770–1827)

CD 2 track 6

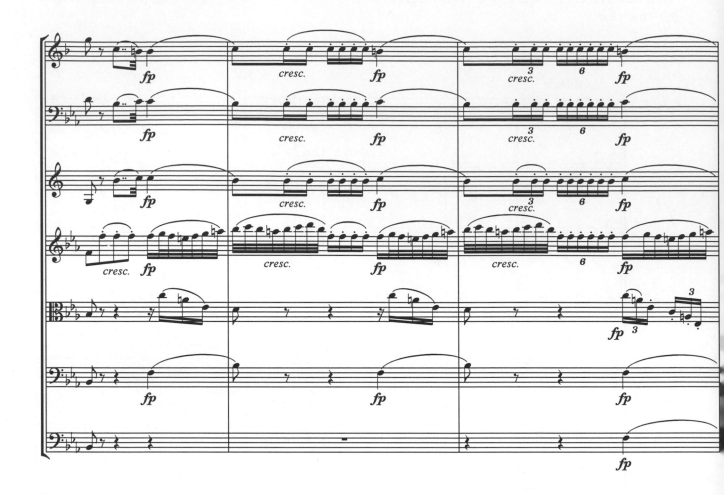

Allegro con brio

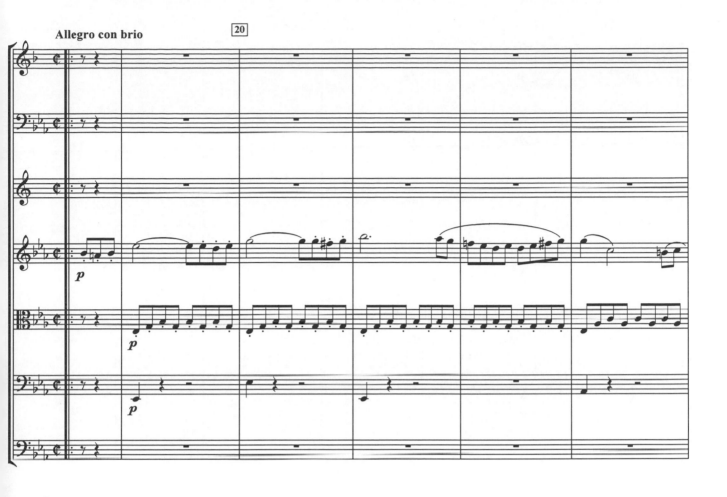

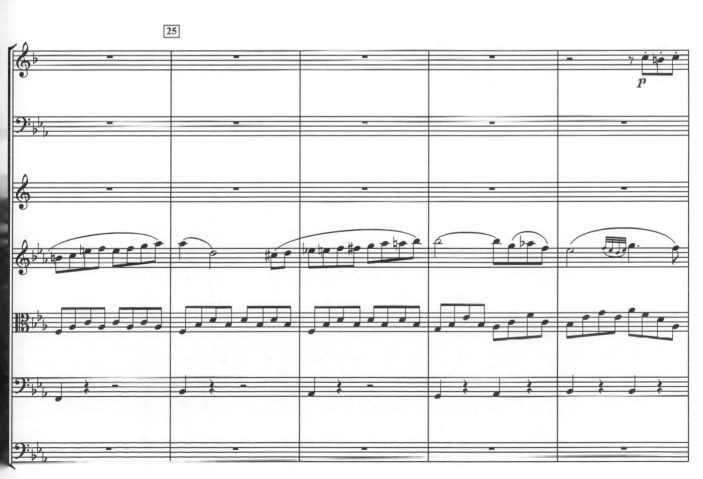

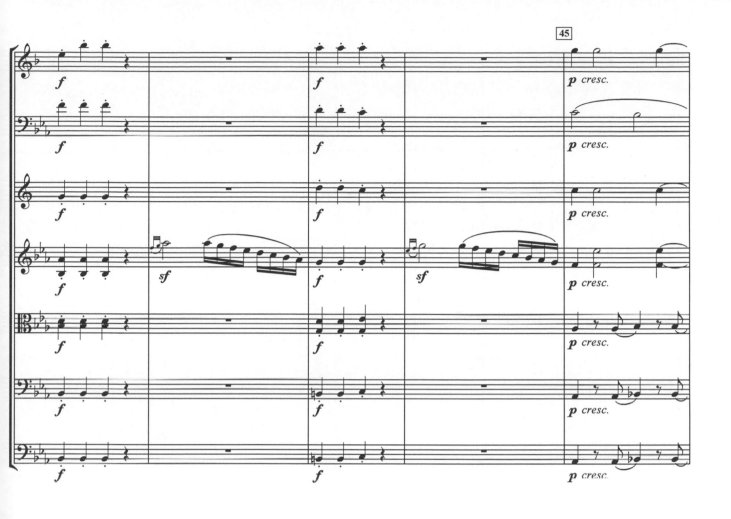

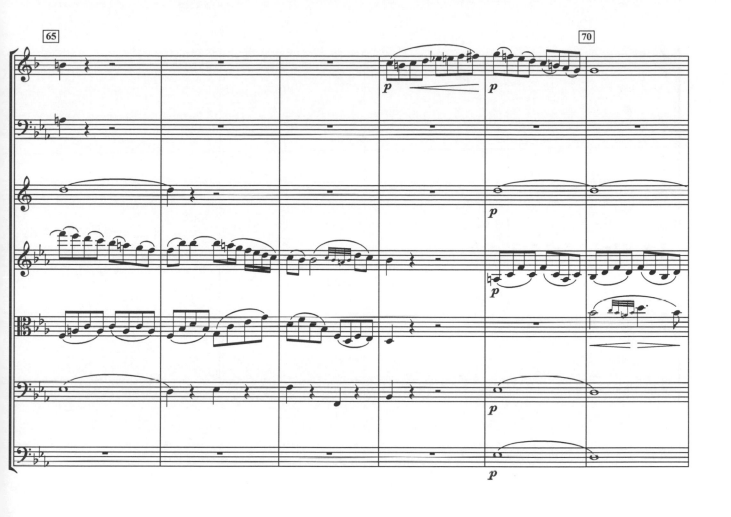

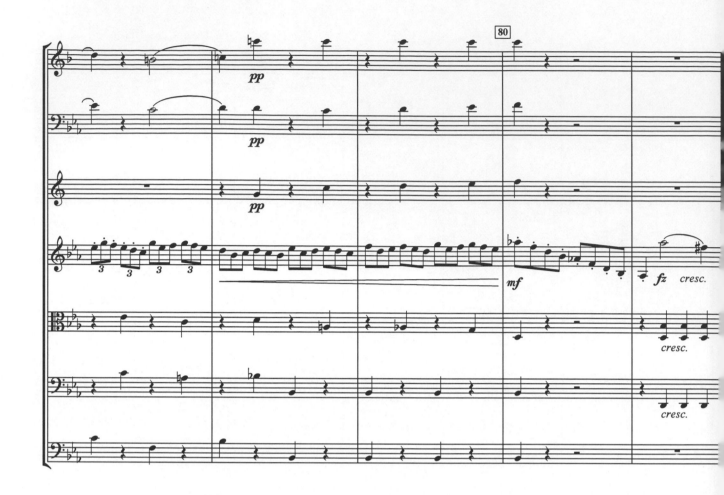

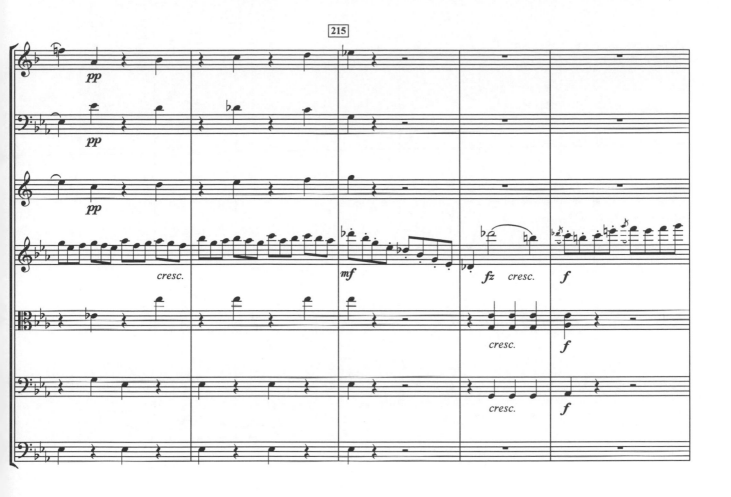

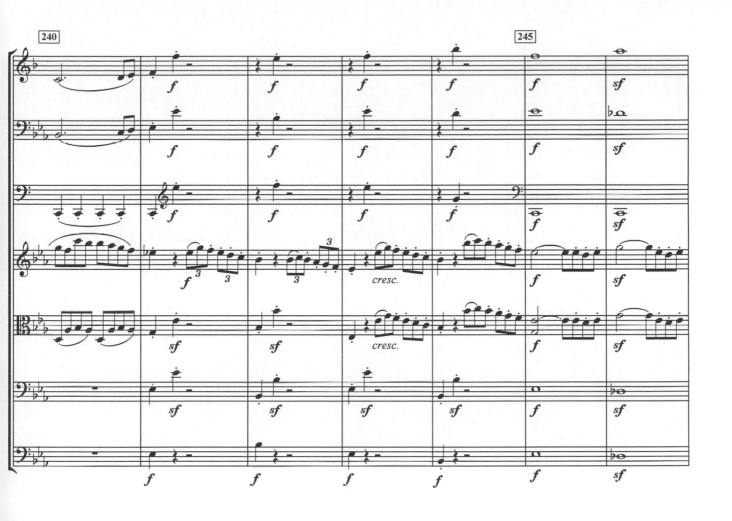

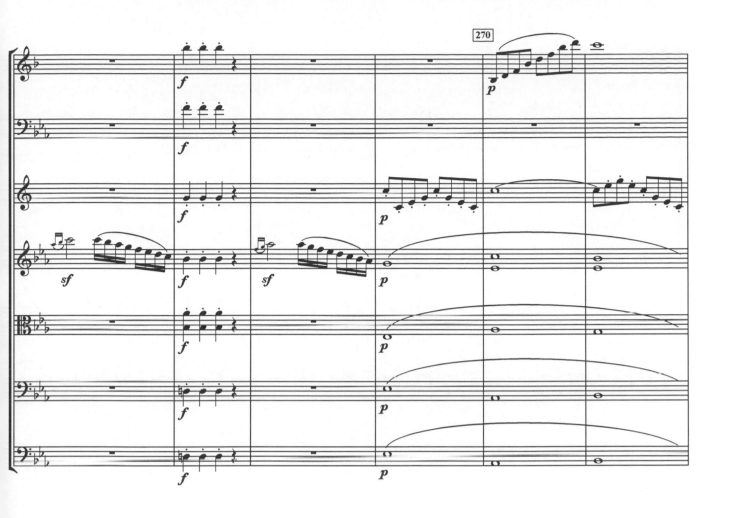

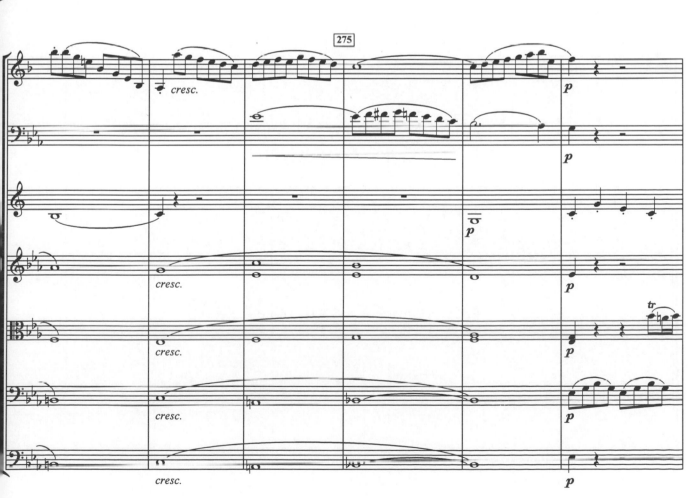

18 Piano Quintet in F minor, Op. 34: movement III

Johannes Brahms (1833–1897)

CD 2 track 7

235

Scherzo da Capo sin al Fine

19 Sonata for Horn, Trumpet and Trombone: movement I

CD 2 track 8

Francis Poulenc (1899–1963)

Cédez peu à peu
Lent

Keyboard Music

20 Pavana Lachrimae

Jan Pieterszoon Sweelinck (1562–1621)

CD 2 track 9

246

21 Partita No. 4 in D, BWV 828: Sarabande and Gigue Johann Sebastian Bach (1685–1750)
CD 2 tracks 10–11

SARABANDE

GIGUE

252

22 Piano Sonata in B♭, K.333: movement I

CD 2 track 12

Wolfgang Amadeus Mozart (1756–1791)

257

23 Kinderscenen, Op. 15: Nos. 1, 3 and 11
CD 2 tracks 13–15

Robert Schumann (1810–1856)

1. VON FREMDEN LÄNDERN UND MENSCHEN
Of Foreign Lands and Peoples

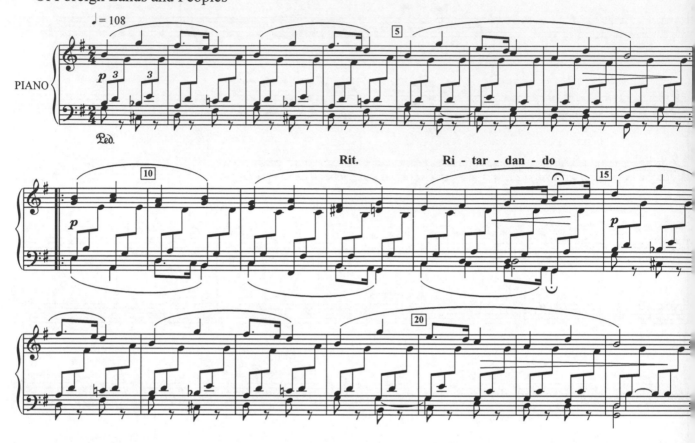

3. HASCHE-MANN
Catch-me-if-you-can

11. FÜRCHTENMACHEN
Frightening

259

24 Pour le piano: Sarabande

CD 2 track 16

Claude Debussy (1862–1918)

261

25 Prelude and Fugue in A, Op. 87 No. 7

CD 2 tracks 17–18

Dmitry Shostakovich (1906–1975)

PRELUDE

FUGUE

Allegretto ($\eivel$ = 92)

26 O Wilhelme, pastor bone

John Taverner (*c*.1495–1545)

CD 3 track 1

You will notice some differences between the printed text of 'O Wilhelme, pastor bone' and the accompanying recording. This is because the piece is found in 16th-century manuscripts which have been interpreted differently by two separate editors. Notice in particular how the editors disagree slightly about the tenor part, which they have had to 'compose' because it is missing from the 16th-century manuscripts. Questions in an examination will refer to the printed version, and would not require you to remember how this deviates from the recording.

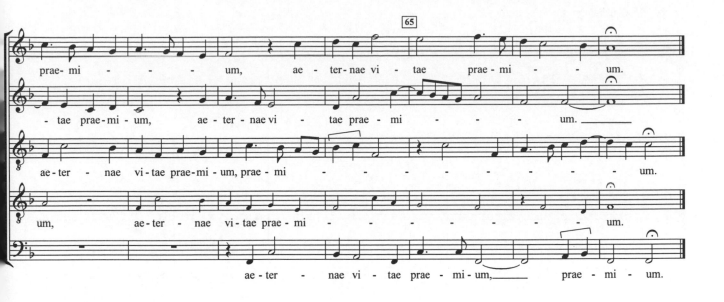

27 In ecclesiis

Giovanni Gabrieli (*c.*1555–1612)

CD 3 track 2

All of the *soli* parts are performed by male voices on the recording.
The alto line is sung at the notated pitch – in a high tenor register.

al - le-lu - ja, al - le - lu - ja.

- lu - ja, al - le - lu - ja.

- lu - ja, al - le - lu - ja.

- lu - ja, al - le-lu - ja.

- lu - ja, al - le - lu - ja.

CORNETTO I SINFONIA

CORNETTO II SINFONIA

CORNETTO III SINFONIA

VIOLA SINFONIA

TROMBONE I SINFONIA

TROMBONE II SINFONIA

C. T. SOLO

De - us

-ja, al - le - lu - ja,

-ja, al - le - lu - ja,

al - le - lu - ja.

al - le - lu - ja.

al - le - lu - ja.

al - le - lu - ja.

281

28 Cantata No. 48, 'Ich elender Mensch': movements I–IV

Johann Sebastian Bach (1685–1750)

CD 3 tracks 3–6

100
e - len - der Mensch, wer wird mich er - lö - - -
Ich e - len - der Mensch, wer wird mich er - lö -
Lei - be die-ses To - - des, ich e - len - der Mensch, wer wird mich er -
- sen vom Lei - be die - ses To - des, ich e - len - der Mensch, wer
105
110
S.
- sen, wer wird mich er - lö - sen,
A.
- sen, wer wird mich er - lö - sen,
T.
- lö - - sen, er - lö - sen,
B.
wird mich er - lö - sen, er - lö - sen,
Vln. I
Vln. II
Vla.
Cont.

2. Recitativo

O Schmerz,— o E-lend! so mich trifft, in dem der Sün-dern Gift bei mir in Brust und A-dern wü-thet. Die Welt wird mir ein Siech-und Ster-be-haus, der Leib muss sei-ne Pla-gen bis zu dem Gra-be mit sich tra-gen. Al-ein die see-le füh-let das stärk-ste Gift, da-mit sie an-ge-ste-cket: d'rum, wenn der Schmerz den Leib des To-des trifft, wenn ihr der Kreuz-kelch bit-ter schme-cket, so treibt er ihr ein brün-stig seuf-zen aus.

3. Chorale

Tpt, Obs, Vln I/S. Vln II/A.

Vla/T. Cont./B.

Soll's ja so sein, dass Straf' und Pein auf Sün-dern fol-gen müs - sen: so fahr' hier fort und

scho - ne dort, und lass mich hier wohl büs - - - sen.

4. Aria

Oboe Solo

Continuo

Alto

Ach

le - ge das So - dom der sünd-li-chen Glie-der, wo-fern es dein Wil - le,

wo-fern es dein Wil - le, zer - stö - ret dar - nie - der!

Ach

297

le - ge das So - dom der sünd - li-chen Glie - der, wo - fern es dein Wil - le, zer -

- stö - ret dar - nie-der!

Nur scho - ne der see - le, und ma - che sie rein, um

vor dir ein hei - li - ges Zi - on zu sein.

Nur scho - ne der see - le, und ma - che sie rein, nur scho - ne der -

seele, und mache sie rein, um vor dir ein heiliges Zion zu sein,

D.C. al Fine

um vor dir ein heiliges Zion zu sein.

29 'Quoniam tu solus' *from* The Nelson Mass

Joseph Haydn (1732–1809)

CD 3 track 7

SOPRANO SOLO — Quoniam tu solus, solus sanctus,   Tu

SOPRANO — Tu, tu solus, solus Dominus,

ALTO — Tu, tu solus, solus Dominus,

TENOR — Tu, tu solus, solus Dominus,

BASS — Tu, tu solus, solus Dominus,

ORCHESTRA (Piano reduction)

304

30 Locus iste

Anton Bruckner (1824–1896)

CD 3 track 8

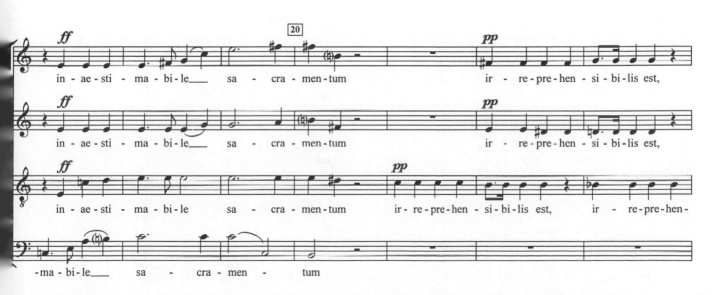

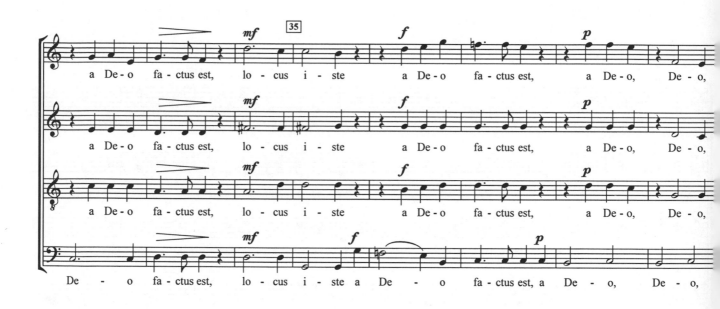

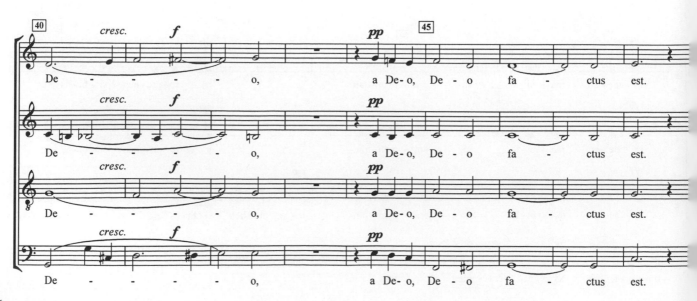

31 Symphony of Psalms: movement III

CD 3 track 9

Igor Stravinsky (1882–1971)

308

309

310

318

319

326

328

135

338

342

32 The Lamb

CD 3 track 10

John Tavener (b. 1944)
text: William Blake

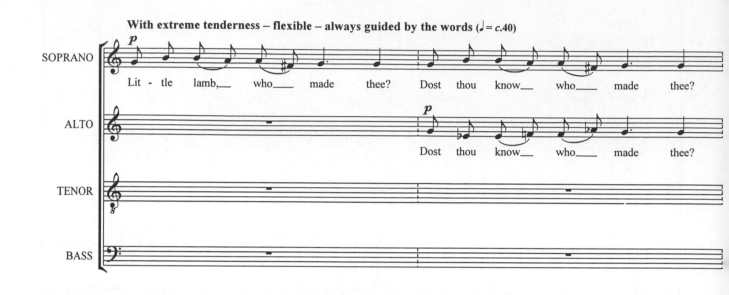

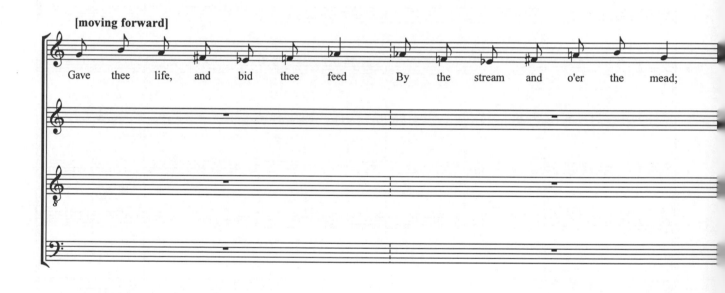

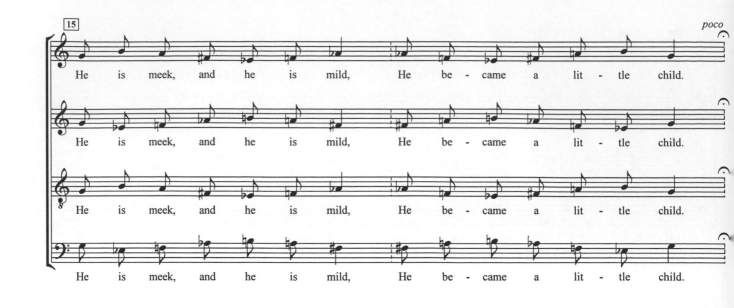

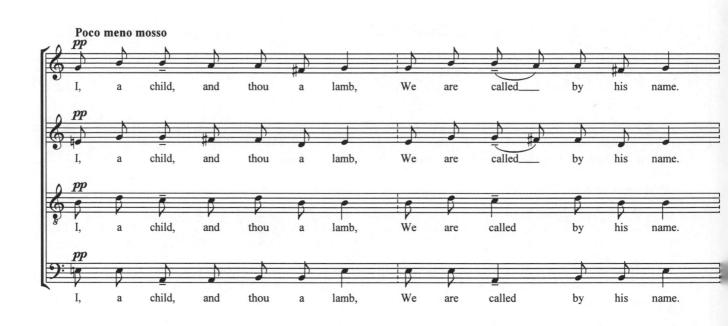

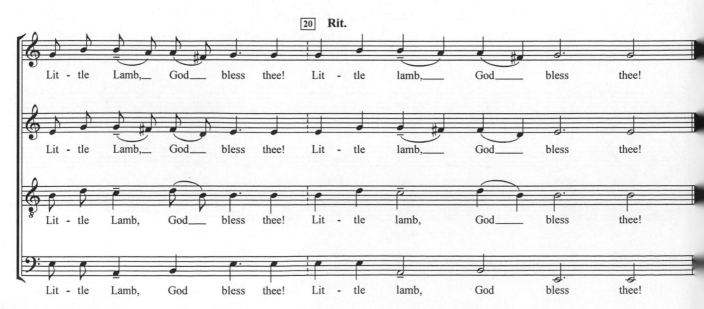

33 Flow my tears

John Dowland (*c.*1563–1626)

CD 3 track 11

The recording on the accompanying CD expands the instrumentation to include
a bass viol. The pitch is approximately a tone lower than modern pitch.

dayes, *my wear - ie dayes* Of all joyes have de - pri - ved.
- serts, *for my de - serts* Are my hopes, since hope is gone.

Harke you sha - dowes that in darck - nesse dwell, Learne to con - temne light.

Hap - pie, hap - pie they that in hell Feele

not the world's de - spite.

34 Sing we at pleasure

CD 3 track 12

Thomas Weelkes (*c.*1575–1623)

351

35 Ohimè, se tanto amate

Claudio Monteverdi (1567–1643)
text: Giovanni Battista Guarini

36 'Thy hand, Belinda' and 'When I am laid in earth' *from* Dido and Aeneas

Henry Purcell (1659–1695)

CD 3 track 14

The pitch on the accompanying CD is approximately a semitone lower than modern concert pitch.

re - mem - ber me,   but ah!_____ for - get   my fate,   re - mem - ber me,   but

Ritornelle

ah!_____ for - get   my_ fate.

37 My mother bids me bind my hair

Joseph Haydn (1732–1809)
text: Anne Hunter

CD 3 track 15

1. My mo - ther_ bids me bind_ my hair with bands_ of_ ro - sy hue, tie
2. 'Tis sad_ to_ think the days_ are gone, when those_ we_ love_ were near, I

up_ my sleeves with rib - bands rare and lace my bo - dice blue,
sit_ up - on this mos - sy stone and sigh when none_ can hear,

tie up__ my sleeves with rib-bands rare and lace,__ and lace my__ bo-dice__ blue!
I sit__ up-on this mos-sy stone and sigh,__ and sigh when__ none can__ hear.

For why, she cries, sit still and weep, while o-thers dance and
And while I spin my fla-xen thread and sing my sim-ple

play? A-las! I scarce can go or creep, while Lu-bin is a-
lay, the vil-lage seems a-sleep or dead: now Lu-bin is a-

way, a-las! I scarce can go or creep, while Lu-bin__ is a-
way, the vil-lage seems a-sleep or dead: now Lu-bin__ is a-

way, while Lu-bin is__ a-way, is a-way, is a-way.
way, now Lu-bin is__ a-way, is a-way, is a-way.

38 Der Doppelgänger

CD 3 track 16

Franz Schubert (1797–1828)
text: Heinrich Heine

Still ist die Nacht, es ru - hen die Gas - sen,

in die - sem_ Hau - se wohn - te mein_ Schatz; sie hat schon

längst_ die Stadt ver - las - sen, doch steht noch das Haus_ auf dem sel - ben

Platz. Da steht auch ein Mensch, und starrt in die Hö - he.

cresc. poco a poco

und ringt die Hän - de vor Schmer - zens-ge - walt; ____ mir ____ graust es,

wenn ich sein Ant -litz se - he, der Mond zeigt mir mei - ne eig' - ne Ge - stalt. ____

Du Dop - pel - gän - ger, du blei -cher Ge - sel - le! was äffst du nach mein

Lie - be -lied, das mich ge - quält auf die - ser Stel - le so man - che

Nacht, in al - ter Zeit?

39 Après un rêve

Gabriel Fauré (1845–1924)
text: Romain Bussine

Dans un som - meil__ que char - mait ton i - ma - ge Je rê - vais le bon-

-heur ar - dent mi - ra - - ge, Tes yeux é - taient plus doux,__ ta voix pure et so - no - - re,

Tu ray - on - nais comme un ciel__ é - clai - ré par l'au - ro - - re; Tu m'ap - pe -

- lais__ et je quit - tais la ter - - re Pour m'en - fuir a - vec toi vers la lu - miè - - re,

Les cieux pour__ nous__ entr'ouvraient leurs nu - es, splen - deurs_____ in - con - nu - es, lu - eurs di - vi - nes en - tre-

40 'Der kranke Mond' *from* Pierrot Lunaire

CD 3 track 18

Arnold Schoenberg (1874–1951)
text: Albert Giraud trans. Otto Erich Hartleber

Pfühl,___ dein Blick, so fie-bernd ü-ber-gross, bannt mich, wie frem-de Me-lo-

- die._____ An un - still - ba - rem

Lie - bes-leid stirbst du, an Sehn-sucht, tief er-stickt, du näch - tig to-des-kran-ker

Mond,___ dort___ auf des Him-mels schwar-zem Pfühl.___

Den Lieb - sten, der im Sin-nen-rausch___ ge-dan-ken-los zur Lieb-sten geht, be-lus-tigt dei-ner Strah-len Spiel, dein

(im Ton genau so wie der vorhergehende Takt)   (dieser Takt anders, aber doch nicht tragisch!!)

Schluss
des I
Teils.

blei-ches, qual-ge-bor-nes Blut, du näch-tig to - des-kran-ker Mond!

41 'Summertime' *from* Porgy and Bess

CD 3 track 19

George Gershwin (1898–1937)
text: Dubose Heyward

hush, lit - tle ba - by, don'_ yo' cry._____

poco animato

mf espr.

poco rit.

Tempo 1

One of these morn - in's   you goin' to rise_ up sing - in',_____ Then you'll

WOMEN'S VOICES   *p espr.*

Ooh_____   ooh_____

Tempo 1

Solo Violin

poco rit.

pp

spread yo'   wings_   an' you'll take_ the   sky._____ But till that

ooh_____

ooh   ooh_____   ooh_ ooh

42 Passport To Pimlico (1948): The Siege of Burgundy

Georges Auric

CD 4 track 1

This score follows the 3-stave form of the composer's own short score.

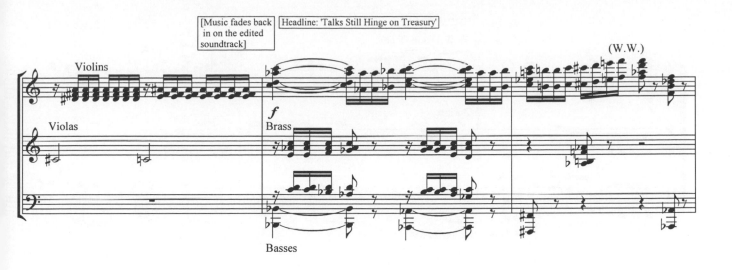

[Music fades back in on the edited soundtrack]

Headline: 'Talks Still Hinge on Treasury'

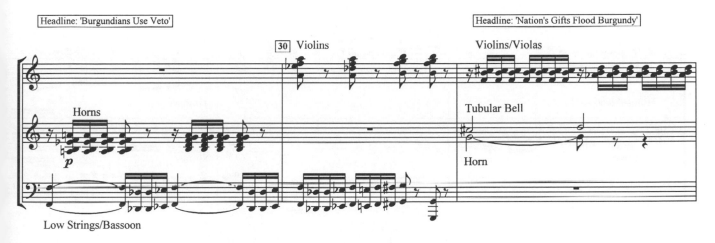

Headline: 'Burgundians Use Veto'

Headline: 'Nation's Gifts Flood Burgundy'

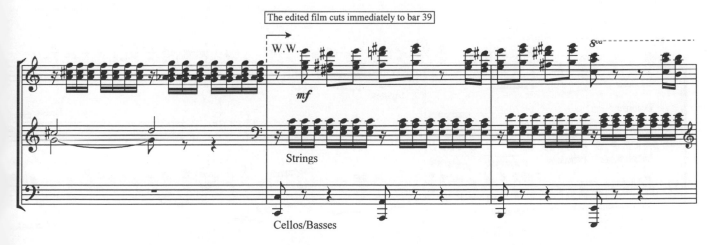

The edited film cuts immediately to bar 39

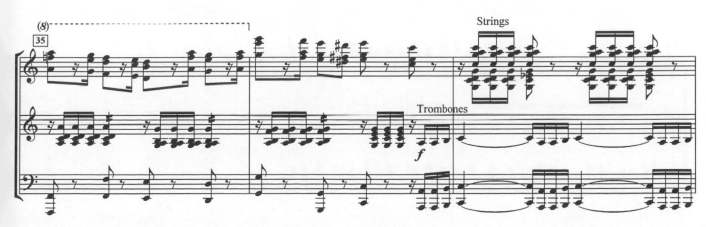

372

43 On the Waterfront (1954): Symphonic Suite (opening)

Leonard Bernstein

CD 4 track 2

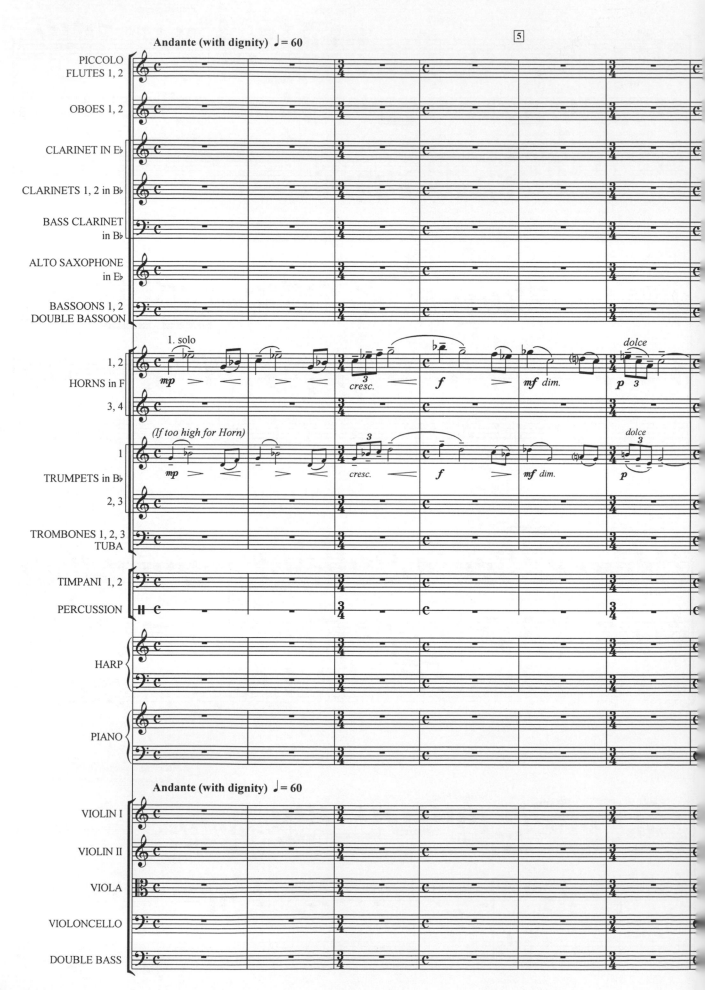

374

* If there are enough timpani available, it is preferable that these two notes (¹B♮ & B♭: ²G & F♯) be played on two separate drums.

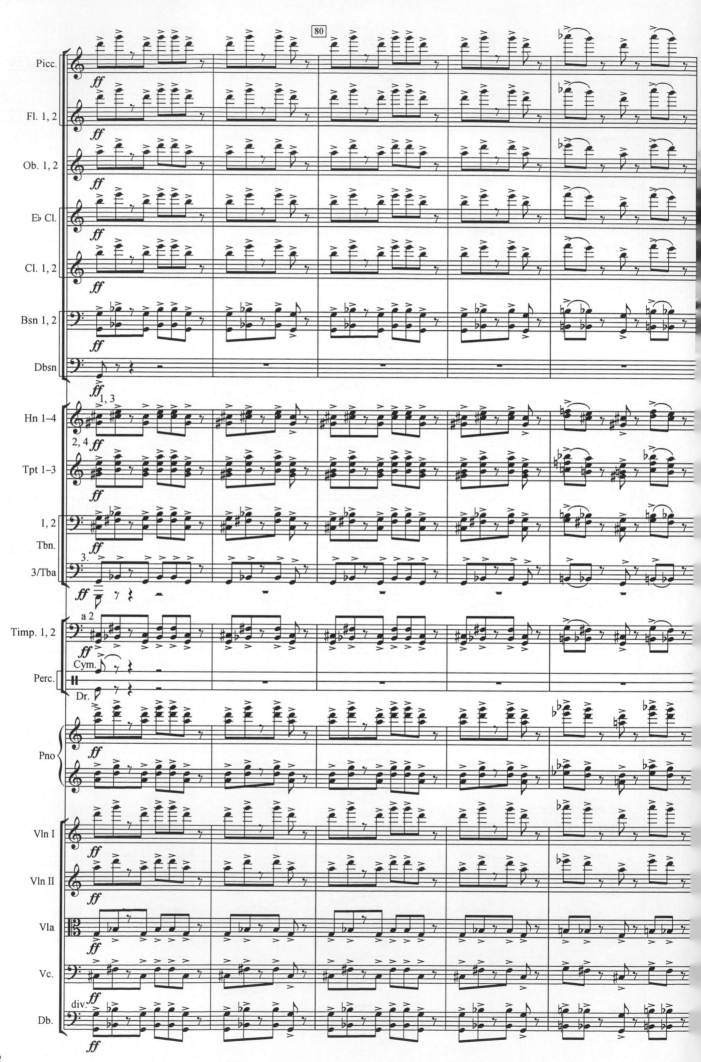

383

44 Planet of the Apes (1968): The Hunt (opening)

Jerry Goldsmith

CD 4 track 3

Where the oboe parts are marked 'E.H.' ('English horn') they are to be played on cor anglais, sounding a fifth lower.

392

393

396

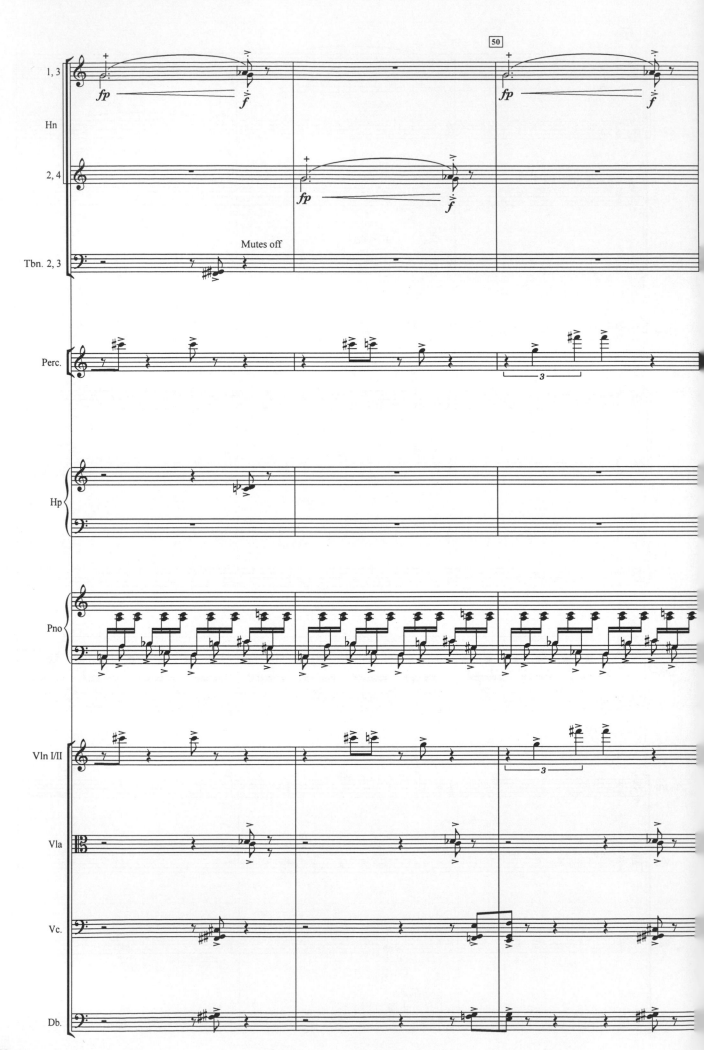

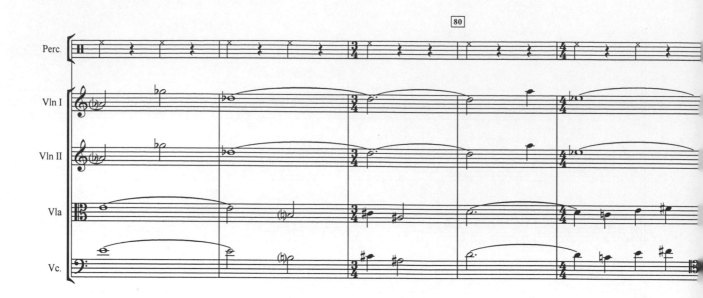

408

45 ET (1982): Flying Theme

John Williams

CD 4 track 4

411

415

417

418

424

425

429

46 Morse on the Case (1986)

CD 4 track 5

Barrington Pheloung

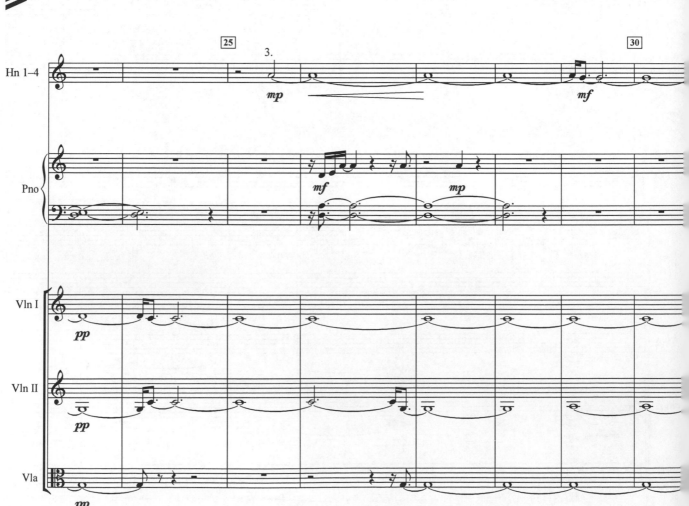

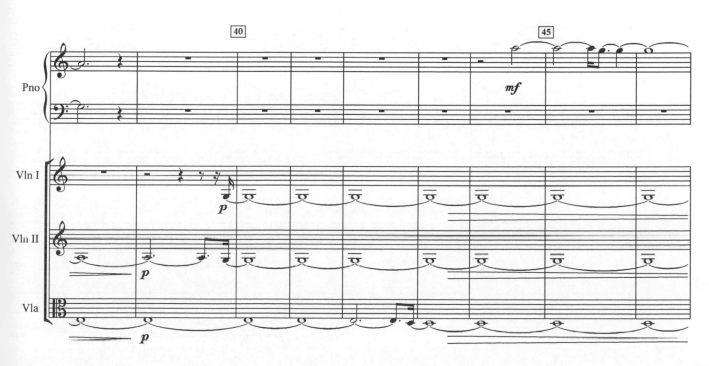

47 Titanic (1997): 'Take her to sea, Mr Murdoch'

James Horner

CD 4 track 6

443

451

454

458

48 West End Blues

as recorded by Louis Armstrong and his Hot Five, 1928
CD 4 track 7

Joe Oliver and Clarence Williams

Add Rhythmic Milk Bottle Sound

Louis Armstrong Scat Vocal

Wa wa wa___ (etc.

Percussion ends

49 Black and Tan Fantasy

as recorded by Duke Ellington and his Orchestra, 1927
CD 4 track 8

Duke Ellington and Bubber Miley

All instruments are shown at concert pitch.

50 Four

Miles Davis

as recorded by the Miles Davis Quintet, 1964
CD 4 track 9

Bars are numbered in 32-bar sections, prefixed by H (for 'head'),
1 (for 1st chorus) or 2 (2nd chorus).

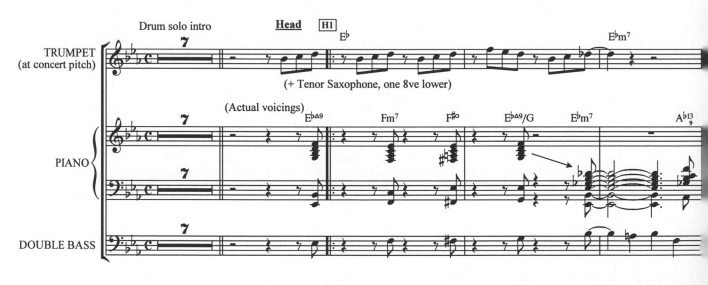

51 I'm Leavin' You

as recorded by Howlin' Wolf, 1959
CD 4 track 10

Chester Burnett (Howlin' Wolf)

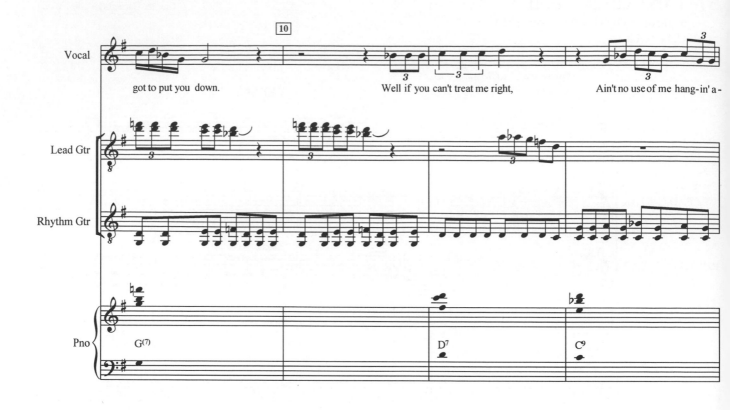

got to put you down.   Well if you can't treat me right,   Ain't no use of me hang-in' a-

VERSE 2 ('stop' chorus)

- round.   Well you told me that you loved me,   You   crossed your heart to die._   But

(2nd time Guitar parts varied ad lib.)

I found out that wasn' so. I'm leav - in' you.
(Baby bye - bye.)
Wo - man I've

got to put you down. Well if you can't treat me right, Ain't no use of me hang - in' a -

VERSE 3 ('stop' chorus)

- round. Well__ ear - ly in the morn - in' be - fore I__ rise,__ You're

lay - in' there rol - lin' your blood - shot eyes.__ You mean__ lit - tle thing, Mean - est

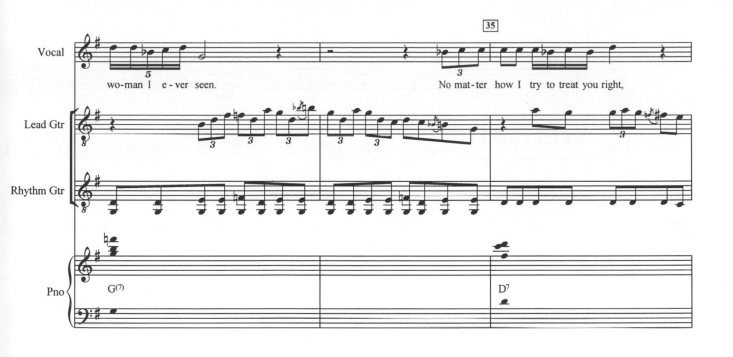

wo-man I e-ver seen.

No mat-ter how I try to treat you right,

2nd time to CODA

GUITAR SOLO
(Band continues shuffle rhythm)

Still__ you're the mean____ lit-tle thing.

Whoo._____

Whoo._____

Harmonica ad lib.

Dal Segno al Coda ⊕ CODA

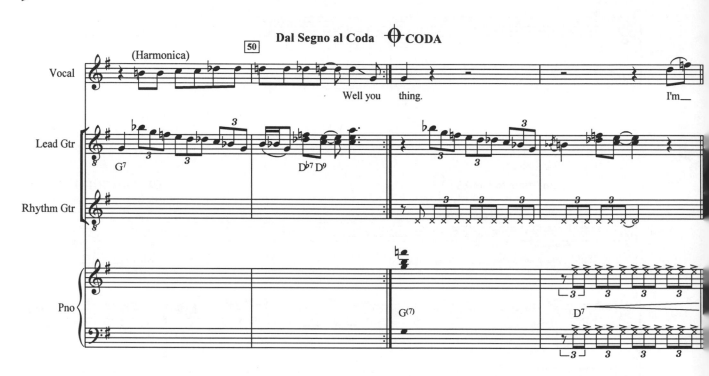

BEGIN FADE OUT . . .

476

52 Honey Don't

Carl Perkins

as recorded by Carl Perkins, 1955
CD 4 track 11

Mm   Ho-ney don't,

481

53 Waterloo Sunset

Ray Davies

as recorded by the Kinks, 1967
CD 4 track 12

484

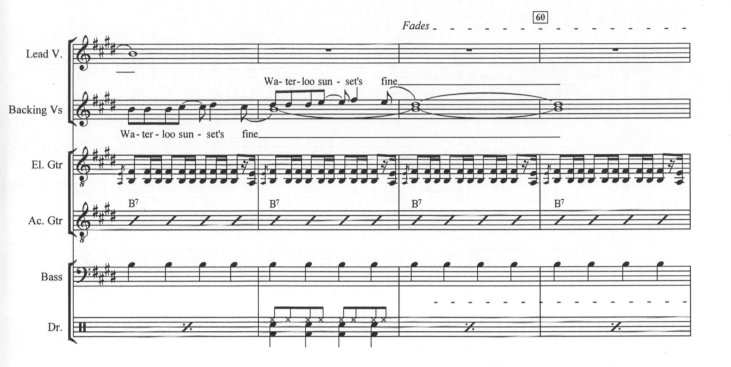

54 A Day in the Life

John Lennon and Paul McCartney

as recorded by the Beatles, 1967
For copyright reasons this recording is not included on the accompanying CD

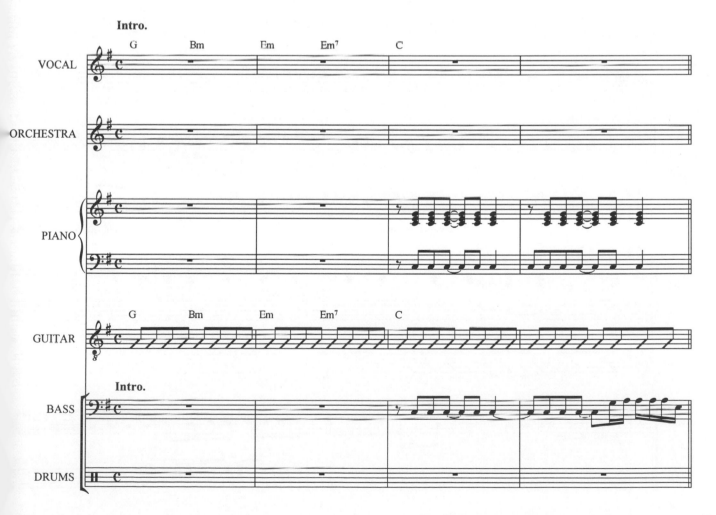

490

Woke up, got out of bed, Dragged a comb a-cross my head,__

Found my way down-stairs and drank a cup And look-ing up__ I no-ticed I was late.

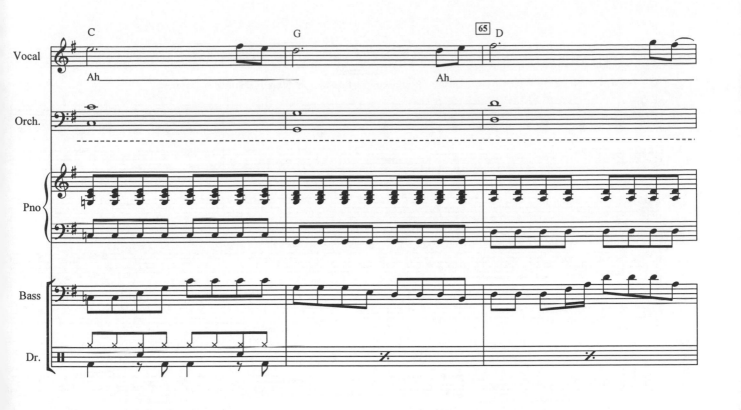

55 You can get it if you really want

as recorded by Desmond Dekker and the Aces, 1970
CD 4 track 13

Jimmy Cliff

498

500

56 Tupelo Honey

as recorded by Van Morrison, 1971
CD 4 track 14

Van Morrison

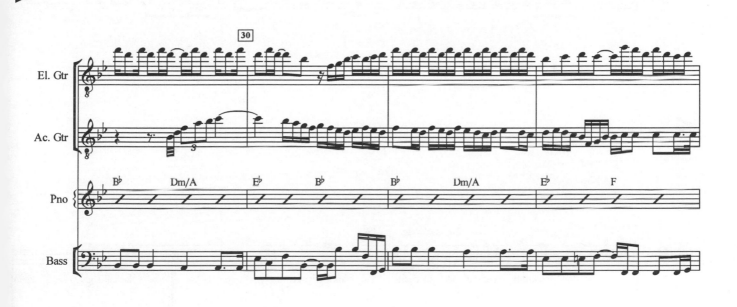

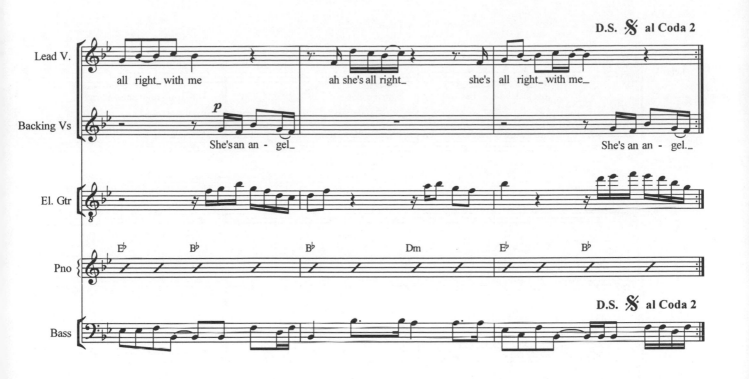

57 Don't look back in anger

as recorded by Oasis, 1996
CD 4 track 15

Noel Gallagher

Slip in - side_ the eye of your mind_____ Don't you know you might find_____ A bet-ter place to play_
Take me to_ the place where you go_____ Where_ no - bo - dy knows_____ If it's night or day_

Vocal: Take that look from off__ your face__ You ain't e - ver gon - na burn__ my___ heart__ out___

And so Sal - ly can wait__ she knows it's too late__

least not to - day.__

58 Rag Bhairav

North Indian

As recorded by Ram Narayan (Sarangi) with Chanranjit Lal Biyavat (Tabla)
CD 4 track 16

The pitch of the recording is slightly less than a perfect 4th higher than notated.
This is because when Indian music is represented in Western notation,
it is conventional to write 'Sa' (corresponding to the tonic note) on C.

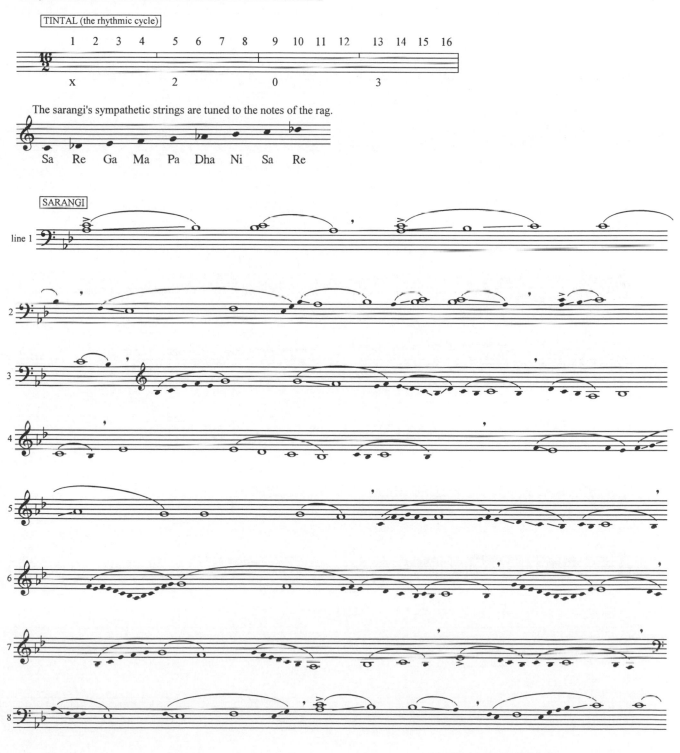

519

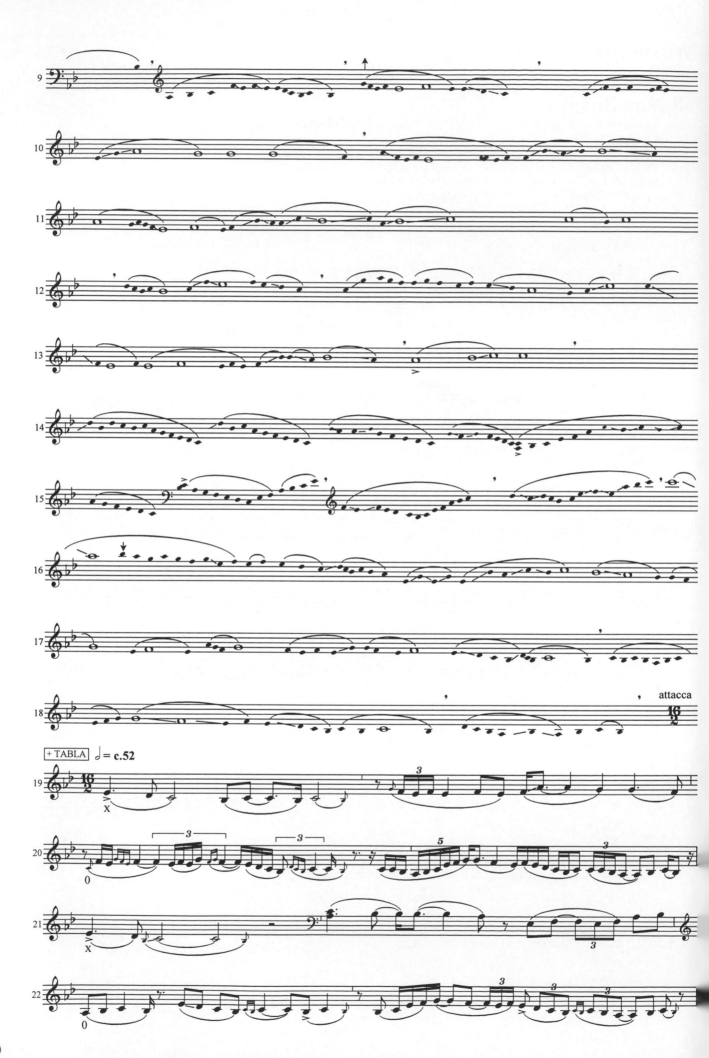

520

59 Baris Melampahan (extract)

traditional Balinese

As recorded by Gong Kebyar de Sebatu
CD 4 track 17

Baris is a standard dance in Bali, usually danced solo but here in a dramatic context. It varies from one village to the next, and is here accompanied by a gamelan gong kebyar, made of bronze and on this recording played extremely fast.

Instruments:

All metallophones are tuned in pairs to create acoustic 'beatings'
Gong - large hanging gong (ends every cycle)
Kempur - smaller hanging gong
Kemong - smallest hanging gong
(bisects each cycle)
Kempli - small horizontally mounted gong
(keeps the pulse)
Jegogan - pair of largest one-octave metallophones
Calung - pair of smaller one-octave metallophones
Ugal - largest two-octave metallophone (melodic leader)
Gangsa: Pemade - two pairs of smaller two-octave metallophones
       Kantilan - two pairs of smallest two-octave metallophones
Reyong - row of 12 horizontally mounted gong chimes
played by four players (unless notated otherwise, reyong III = reyong I,
reyong IV = reyong II)
Kendhang - two-headed drums: 'male' (lanang)
and 'female' (wadon). Kendhang lanang is leader of group and gives signals
Ceng-ceng - small horizontally mounted cymbals
Suling - bamboo flutes (play same as calung)

Scale: Pelog*   5̣ 6̣ 1 2 3 5 6 1̇ 2̇ 3̇   (low → high)

Approximate equivalent pitches:

1   2   3   5   6

Symbols for punctuating instruments:

Gong	◯
Kempur	∨
Kemong	∧
Kempli	+

* Gamelan gong Kebyar are tuned to one of several possible 5-tone modes, derived from the 7-tone pelog scale, in this case the *selisir* mode, the most common, omitting notes 4 and 7.

Sequence:

Intro	kendhang
U x 2	ugal tune
A	angsel (loud)
B x 2	usual tune (loud)
A x 2	angsel (loud)
K	kendhang accents
B x 8	usual tune
A	angsel (loud)
K	kendhang
B x 8	usual tune
A	angsel (loud)
K	kendhang
B x 5	usual tune
A+	angsel (loud) to go 'high'
H x 6	'high' tune
AH	'high' angsel (loud)
BS	usual tune, slower, slowing to end. (Transition to next section)

Angsel: a melodic/rhythmic break cued by the dancer via the drums which get louder before a gong stroke.

Symbols for kendhang (drums):

Lanang	{ ∧	Dug	⟋ Tek
	P	Pak	
Wadon	{ ◯	Dag	
	K	Ka	

(Fades in on gong sound from previous section)

I Intro.

Kendhang lanang   P   ∧   .   P   .   P   P

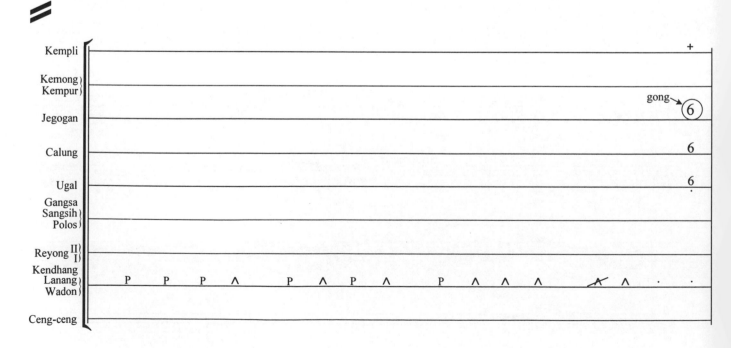

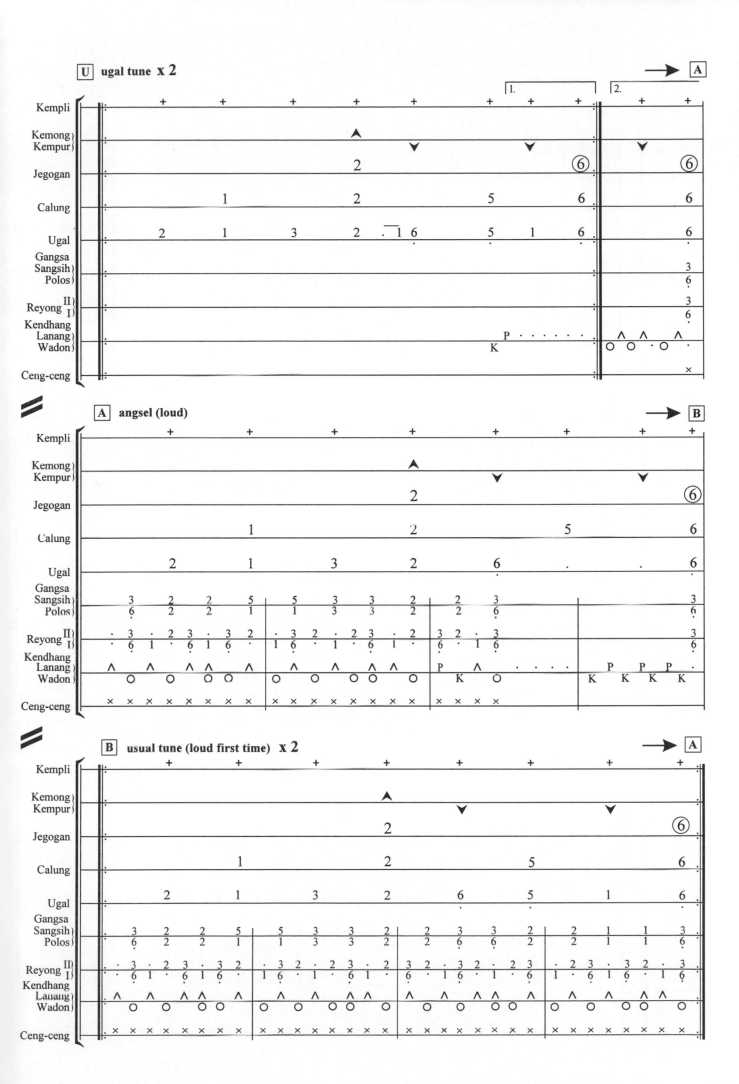

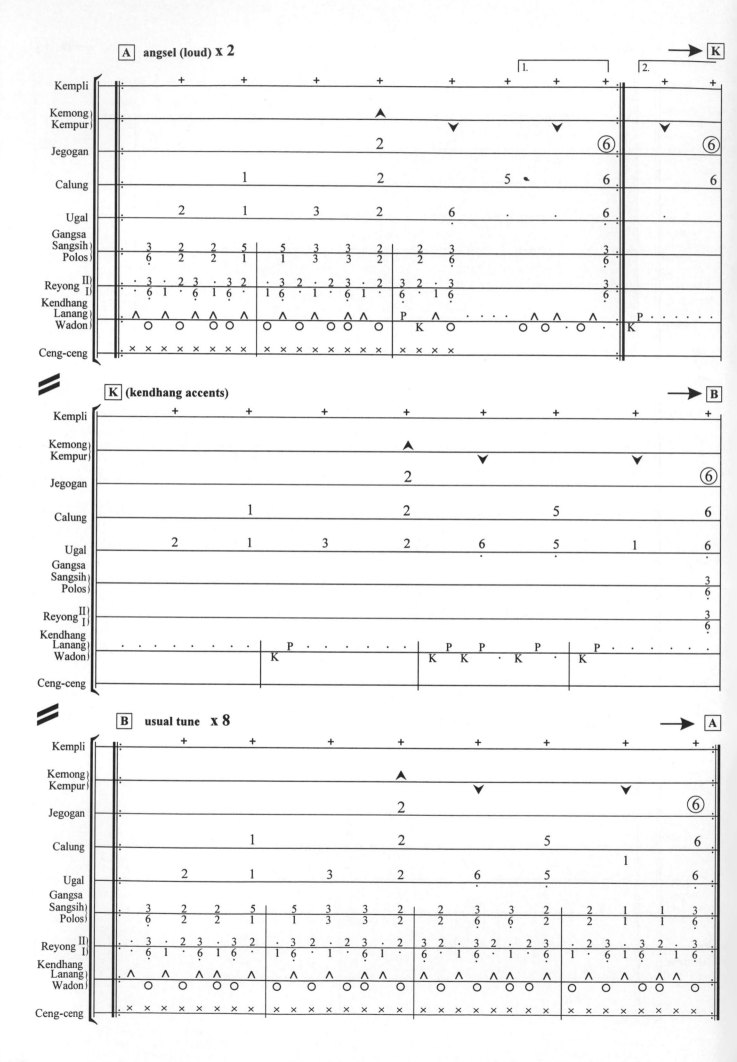

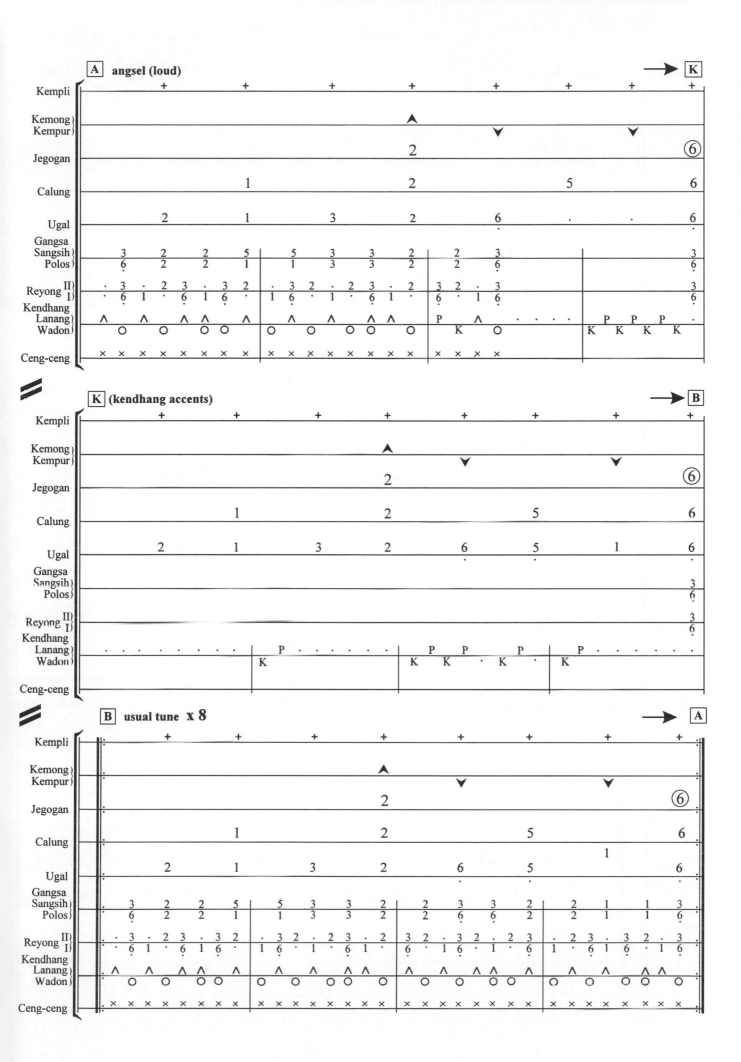

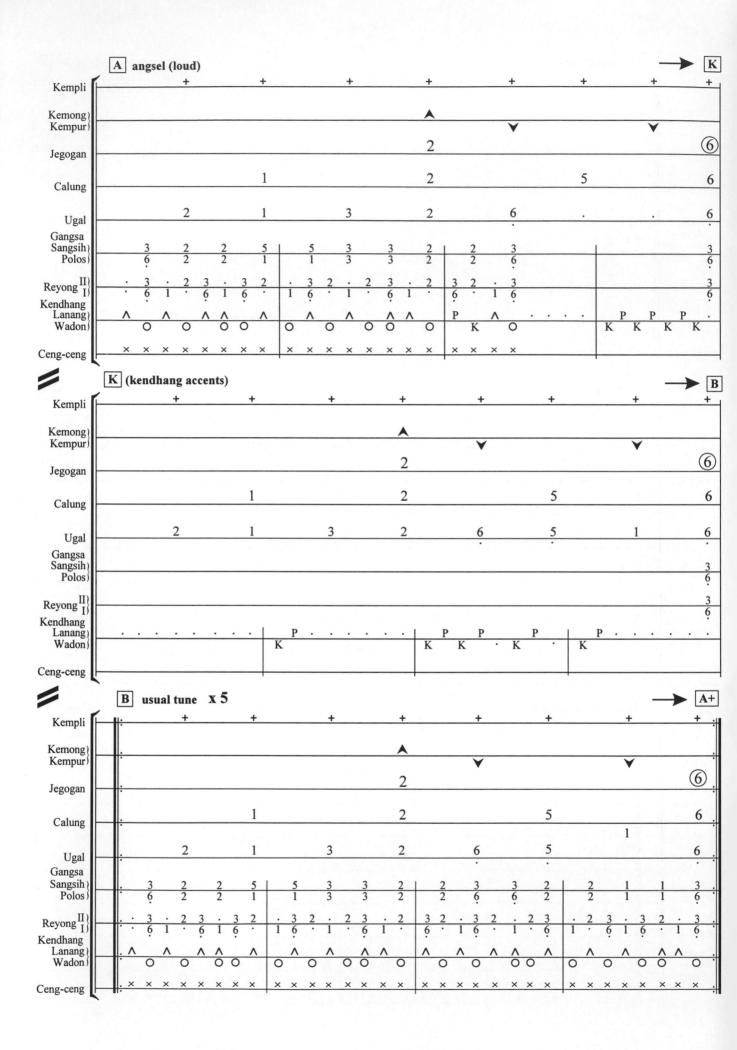

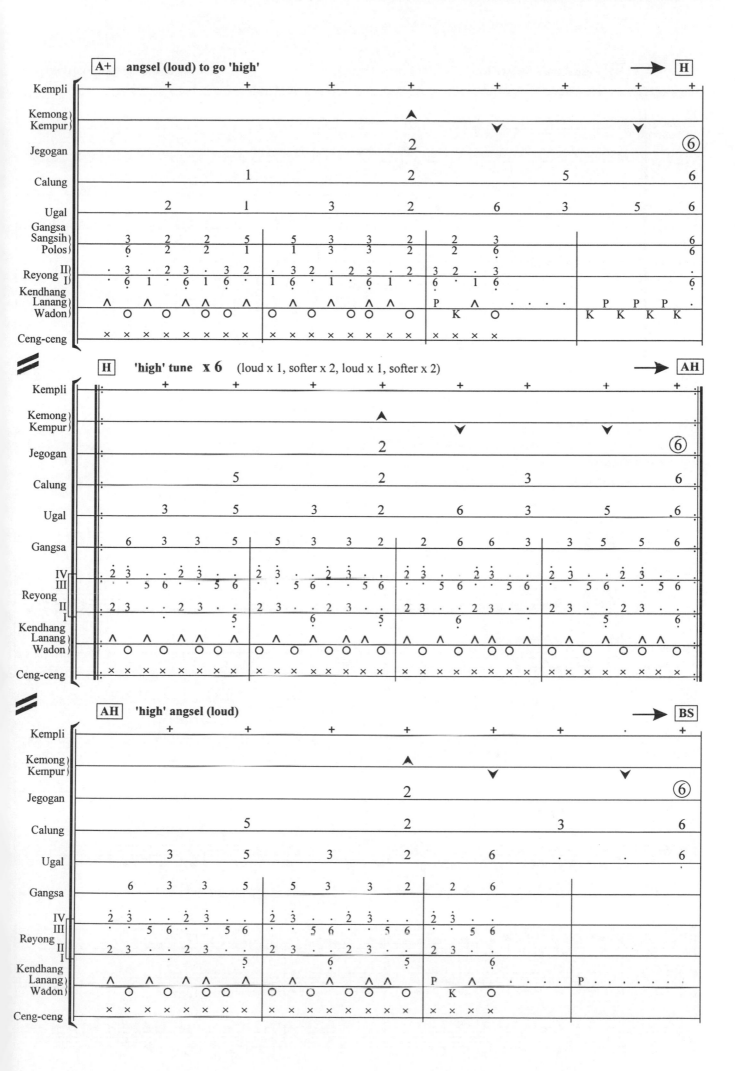

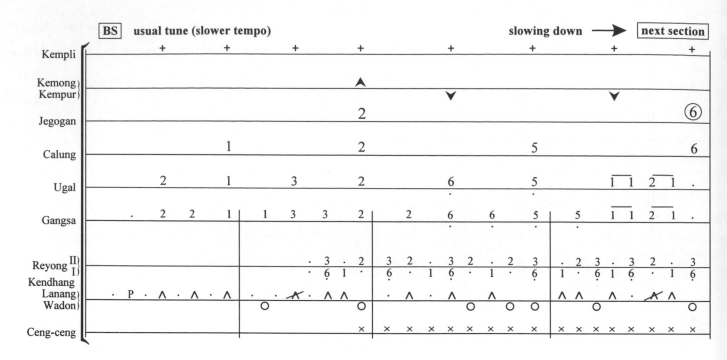

60 Yellow Bird

as recorded by the Red Stripe Ebony Steelband
CD 4 track 18

traditional

The names of instruments and layout of the pans vary from band to band.

61 Tom McElvogue's (jig) and New Irish Barndance (reel)

as recorded by Niall Keegan
CD 4 track 19

jig: Tom McElvogue
reel: traditional arr. Niall Keegan

Many notes are ornamented beyond what has been notated here. Many are double-tongued and some triple-tongued, with the effect that ♪ sounds ♫ or ♪♪♪, and ♩ sounds ♫ or even ♫♫ . This increases the effect of the asymmetric accents in bar 122 and, as a characterization of this style of wind-playing, should be used freely. Foot-tapping occurs on every main beat.

62 Agbekor Dance

as recorded by Mustapha Tettey Addy
CD 4 track 20

traditional Ewe

This music is from the Ewe people of Ghana. None of the instruments have clearly defined pitches, but they have relative pitches
and are carefully tuned according to the piece being played. The transcription uses the closest pitches to be found on traditional staff notation.
Cross-heads show when the wood of the drum has been hit. Normal note-heads indicate 'free beats', produced by hitting the stick on the
drum-skin so that it bounces off immediately. Muted beats are either produced by holding the stick down on the skin once it has been hit,
or by holding one stick down on the skin while striking it with the other stick.

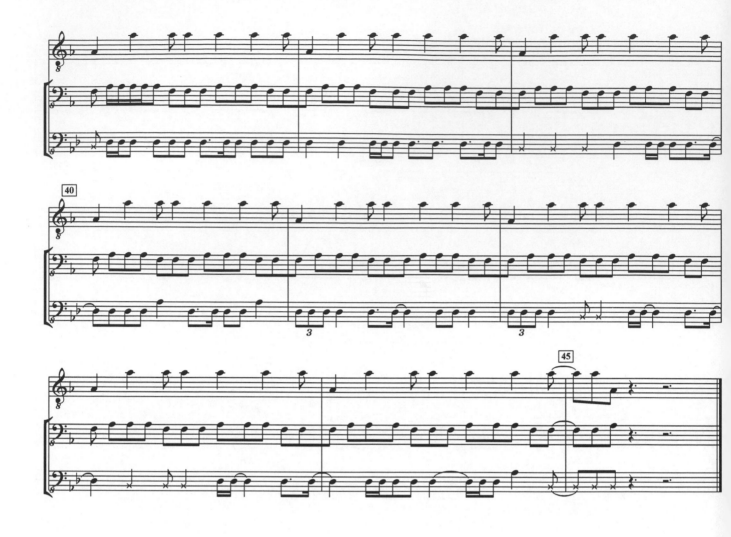

63 Se quema la chumbambá

as recorded by Familia Valera Miranda
CD 4 track 21

Familia Valera Miranda

Cuatro: a guitar-like instrument with four
pairs of metal strings tuned in octaves.

This 4-bar passage (bars 9–12) is the basis of the rest of the song.

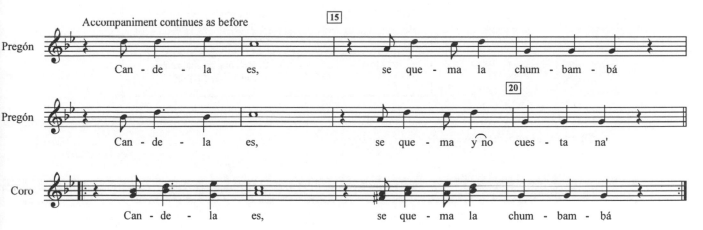

Pregón	Mamá que me estoy quemando, mamá mira que me quemo En no quemándome yo, que se queme el mundo entero
Coro	Candela es, se quema la chumbambá Candela es, se quema la chumbambá
Pregón	Candela es, se quema la chumbambá Candela es, se quema la chumbambá
Coro	Candela es, *etc.*
Pregón	Que se queme la sabana, se queman los sabaneros En no quemándome yo, que se queme el mundo entero
Coro	Candela es, *etc.*

Pregón	Que se queme esta familia, que se queme este tresero,
	En no quemándome yo, que se queme el mundo entero
Coro	Candela es, *etc.*
Pregón	Candela es, se quema la chumbambá
	Candela es, se quema y no cuesta na'
Coro	Candela es, *etc.*

Cuatro solo

Coro	Candela es, se quema la chumbambá
	Candela es, se quema la chumbambá
Pregón	Candela es, se quema la chumbambá
	Candela es, se quema y no cuesta na'
Coro	Candela es, *etc.*
Pregón	Mamá que se queme Emilia, se queman los sabaneros
	En no quemándome yo, que se queme el mundo entero
Coro	Candela es, se quema la chumbambá
	Candela es, se quema la chumbambá
	Candela es, se quema la chumbambá

Cuatro solo	First 21 4-bar cycles	Cuatro improvises over the 4-bar bass/chord pattern. The first six 4-bar cycles are shown below.
	Next 7 4-bar cycles	Bongo improvises while cuatro plays the regular riff (as in bars 9–12)
	Last 2 4-bar cycles	Cuatro plays vocal refrain to cue singers' return.

Opening of cuatro solo

536

Glossary of foreign terms

The list below does not aim to be comprehensive; terms thought to be standard or self-explanatory have not been included.

A

accordez (*Fr.*) .... tune (e.g., the strings of a harp)
allmählich im Zeitmass
    etwas zurückhaltend (*Ger.*) ... gradually holding back the tempo somewhat
ancora più mosso (*It.*) .... still more movement (even quicker)
au mouvement (*Fr.*) .... return to the principal tempo
au second plan (*Fr.*) .... in the background

B

belebend (*Ger.*) .... becoming animated
belebt (*Ger.*) .... animated
ben cant[ato]. (*It.*) .... well-sung
bien piqué (*Fr.*) .... well-detached

C

calando (*It.*) .... becoming quieter
cédez (*Fr.*) .... hold back (i.e., the tempo)
col Viola *ad lib.* (*It.*) .... with the viola part, if desired
cuivré (*Fr.*) .... with a brassy tone

D

Dämpfer auf (*Ger.*) .... mutes on
dans le 1er mouv[emen]t.
    avec plus de langueur (*Fr.*) ... at the initial tempo with greater languor
dans le mouvt. plus animé (*Fr.*).. at the livelier tempo
dieser Takt anders, aber doch
    nicht tragisch!! (*Ger.*) .... [sing] this bar differently, but not tragically!
doppio meno mosso (*It.*) .... at half speed
doux (*Fr.*) .... soft
Dpf. [Dämpfer] Ab (*Ger.*) .... mute(s) off
du talon (*Fr.*) .... at the heel [of the bow]
dura come 3/2 (*It.*) .... lasts as long as 3 minims

E

effacé (*Fr.*) .... unobtrusive
en animant (*Fr.*) .... becoming more lively

G

G.P. .... general pause (i.e., all players are silent)
get[eilt]. (*Ger.*) .... divided (e.g., string parts)

I

im Ton genau so wie der
    vorhergehende Takt (*Ger.*) ... with the same tone as in the previous bar

J

jusqu'à la fin (*Fr.*) .... up to the end

L

langsam und schmachtend (*Ger.*) slowly and languidly
léger (*Fr.*) .... light
légèrement et expressif (*Fr.*) ...... lightly and expressively
lontano (*It.*) .... distant

M

marcatiss[imo]. (*It.*) .... very strongly stressed/accented
mit Dämpfer (*Ger.*) .... with mutes
mouv[emen]t. du début (*Fr.*) ..... at the initial tempo

O

ôtez vite les sourdines (*Fr.*) .... remove the mutes quickly

P

pédale de gauche (*Fr.*) .... left pedal (i.e., the 'soft' pedal on the piano)
perdendosi (*It.*) .... dying away
pincer la corde (*Fr.*) .... pluck the string
piquer lourdement mais *p* (*Fr.*) .. strongly detached, but quietly
più tosto (*It.*) .... rather
plus animé (*Fr.*) .... more lively
position nat[urale]. (*Fr.*) .... at the natural playing position
près de la table (*Fr.*) .... near to the sounding board
pressez peu à peu (*Fr.*) .... quicken gradually

R

re accordez (*Fr.*) .... re-tune (e.g., the strings of a harp)
retenu (*Fr.*) .... held back
rigorosamente (*It.*) .... strictly

S

sans trainer (*Fr.*) .... without dragging
Schluss des I Teils (*Ger.*) .... end of Part I
Schneller (*Ger.*) .... quicker
sehr mässig (*Ger.*) .... at a very moderate pace
sempre come sopra (*It.*) .... always as before
sourdine (*Fr.*) .... mute
soutenu (*Fr.*) .... sustained
sub[ito]. meno *f* e leggiero (*It.*) . suddenly less loud and lightly
sul tasto poco a poco naturale (*It.*) play at the fingerboard, gradually returning to the natural position
sur la touche (*Fr.*) .... at the fingerboard

T

tacet (*It.*) .... remain silent
toujours animé (*Fr.*) .... still lively
toujours en animant (*Fr.*) .... still becoming livelier
très discret (*Fr.*) .... very unobtrusively
très doux – bien chanté (*Fr.*) ...... very soft – well-sung
très en dehors (*Fr.*) .... very prominent
très lié (*Fr.*) .... very smooth (*legato*)
très marqué (*Fr.*) .... very stressed/accented
très modéré (*Fr.*) .... at a very moderate tempo
très précis (*Fr.*) .... very precisely
très sec (*Fr.*) .... very dry
très sonoré (*Fr.*) .... very sonorous

U

un peu (*Fr.*) .... a little
una corda (*It.*) .... one string (i.e., the 'soft' pedal on the piano)

Z

zart (*Ger.*) .... soft

Translations of sung texts

Sacred Vocal Music

26. O Wilhelme, pastor bone

O Wilhelme, pastor bone
Cleri pater et patrone
Mundi nobis in agone
Confer opem et depone
Vitae sordes et coronae
Coelestis da gloriam.

Fundatorem specialem
Serva Thomam Cardinalem
Et ecclesiam piorum
Tueare, custos horum ;
Et utrisque concedatur
Aeternae vitae praemium.

Antiphon in honour of St William of York: written for Cardinal College (now Christ Church College), Oxford

O William, good shepherd, father to the clergy and our protector in this world's strife; grant us your aid and banish the sins of this life, and bring us the joy of a heavenly crown.

Especially, we pray, protect Cardinal Thomas [Wolsey], our founder and, as guardian, watch over this church of devout souls, that both may earn the reward of life eternal.

27. In ecclesiis

In ecclesiis
Benedicite Domino, Alleluia.
In omni loco dominationis (eius)
Benedic anima mea Dominum, Alleluia.
In Deo salutari meo et gloria mea.
Deus auxilium meum et spes mea in Deo est, Alleluia.
Deus noster, te invocamus,
te laudamus, te adoramus.
Libera nos, salva nos, vivifica nos, Alleluia.
Deus adjutor noster in aeternum,
Alleluia, alleluia, alleluia.

Anonymous

In every place where his people gather:
bless the Lord, Alleluia!
In every place within his kingdom,
bless the Lord, my soul, Alleluia!
Rejoice in the Lord, my Saviour and my glory!
God is my helper, and my hope is in God. Allelluia!
God of us all, we invoke your name,
We praise you, we worship you.
Deliver us, save us, grant us life! Alleluia!
God is our helper for evermore.
Alleluia, alleluia, alleluia.

28. Ich elender Mensch

1. Ich elender Mensch, wer wird mich erlösen vom Leibe dieses Todes!?

Romans. vii. 24

1. Unhappy man that I am; who will deliver me from this deathly body?

2. O Schmerz, O Elend! So mich trifft, indem der Sünden Gift bei mire in Brust und Adern wüthet Die Welt wird mir ein Siech und Sterbehaus, der Leib muss seine Plagen bis zu dem Grabe mit sich tragen. Allein, die Seele fühlet das stärkste Gift, damit sie angestecket: d'rum, wenn der Schmerz den Leib des Todes trifft, wenn ihr der Kreuz-kelch bitter schmecket, so treibt er ihr, ein brünstig Seufzen aus.

Anonymous

2. O the pain, O the misery that torment me, as the poison of my sins courses raging through my breast and veins. This world is more and more my infirmary, my death bed; this body must carry its torments to the grave. But my soul feels most strongly the poison that afflicts it, so that, when pain affects this deathly body, when the cup tastes bitter to the soul, it tears from it a heavy sigh.

3. Soll's ja so sein, dass Straf' und Pein
auf Sünden folgen müssen;
so fahr' hier fort und schone dort,
und lass mich hier wohl büssen

Martin Rutilius

3. If it should be, that punishment and tribulation must follow from our sins, then punish me in this world and spare me in the next and let me atone here below.

4. Ach leg das Sodom der sündlichen Glieder,
wofern es dein Wille zerstöret darnieder!
Nur schone der Seele, und mache sie rein,
um vor dir ein heiliges Zion zu sein.

Anonymous

4. Ah, if it should be your will, destroy this Sodom, this sinful body. Spare only the soul and purify it, that it might become your holy Sion.

29. Quoniam tu solus

Quoniam tu solus sanctus,
tu solus Dominus
tu solus Altissimus
Jesu Christe
Cum Sancto Spiritu in gloria Dei Patris, Amen.

For thou only art holy;
Thou only art the Lord;
Thou only, O Christ,
with the Holy Ghost,
art most high in the glory of God the Father, Amen.

From the Gloria (ordinary of the Mass)

30. Locus iste

Locus iste a Deo factus est
inaestimabile sacramentum, irreprehensibilis est

This place was made by God,
a priceless mystery; it is without reproof.

Liber usualis : Gradual for the dedication of a church

31. Symphony of Psalms (movement III)

(Alleluia) Laudate Dominum in sanctis eius: Laudate eum
in firmamento virtutis eius. Laudate eum in virtutibus eius:
laudate eum secundum multitudinem magnitudinis eius.
Laudate eum in sono tubae: laudate eum in psalterio et
cithara. Laudate eum in timpano et choro: laudate eum
in chordis et organo. Laudate eum in cymbalis bene
sonantibus: laudate eum in cimbalis iubilationis: omnis
spiritus laudet Dominum.

Psalm CL

(Alleluia) Praise ye the Lord. Praise God in His
Sanctuary: praise Him in the firmament of His power.
Praise Him for His mighty acts: praise Him according
to His excellent greatness. Praise Him with the sound of
the trumpet: praise Him with the psaltery and the harp.
Praise Him with the timbrel and dance: praise Him with
stringed instruments and organs. Praise Him upon the
loud cymbals: praise Him upon the high sounding
cymbals. Let everything that hath breath praise the
Lord. Praise ye the Lord.

Secular Vocal Music

35. Ohimè, se tanto amate

Ohimè, se tanto amate
Di sentir 'ohimè', deh perchè fate
Chi dice 'ohimè' morire?
S'io moro, un sol potrete
Languido e doloroso 'ohimè' sentire.
Ma se, cor mio, volete
Che vita habbia da voi,
E voi da me havrete
Mill' e mille dolc' 'ohimè'.

Giovanni Battista Guarini

Ah me, my lady, if you so delight
To hear a breathed 'Ah me',
Why then so swiftly doom to endless night
A wretch that breathes 'Ah me'?
For if I die, brief will your pleasure be
To hear one weak and anguished last 'Ah me',
But if you grant me grace, my lady bright,
Then shall you hear my ecstasy
Ten thousand times breathe out a soft 'Ah me'.

38. Der Doppelgänger

Still ist die Nacht, es ruhen die Gassen,
in diesem Hause wohnte mein Schatz;
sie hat schon längst die Stadt verlassen,
doch steht noch das Haus auf demselben Platz.

The night is quiet, the streets are calm,
In this house my beloved lived:
She has long since left the town,
But the house still stands, here in the same place.

Da steht auch ein Mensch und starrt in die Höhe,
und ringt die Hände vor Schmerzensgewalt;
mir graust es, wenn ich sein Antlitz sehe,
der Mond zeigt mir meine eigne Gestalt.

A man stands there also and looks to the sky,
And wrings his hands overwhelmed by pain:
I am terrified catching sight of his face
When, by the light of the moon, I see my own.

Du Doppelgänger, du bleicher Geselle!
Was äffst du nach mein Liebesleid,
das mich gequält auf dieser Stelle
so manche Nacht, in alter Zeit?

O pale comrade, my very double,
Why do you ape the pain of my love
Which tormented me upon this spot
So many a night, so long ago?

Heinrich Heine

39. Après un rêve

Dans un sommeil que charmait ton image
Je rêvais le bonheur, ardent mirage ;
Tes yeux étaient plus doux, ta voix pure et sonore,
Tu rayonnais comme un ciel éclairé par l'aurore ;

Tu m'appelais et je quittais la terre
Pour m'enfuir avec toi vers la lumière,
Les cieux pour nous entr'ouvraient leurs nues,
Splendeurs inconnues, lueurs divines entrevues.

Hélas! hélas, triste reveil des songes,
Je t'appelle, ô nuit, rends-moi tes mensonges,
Reviens, reviens, radieuse,
Reviens, ô nuit mystérieuse!

Romain Bussine

After a Dream

In a sleep charmed by your image
I dreamed of happiness, passionate delusion:
your eyes were softer, your voice pure and full,
you were radiant as a sky lit by the dawn.

You called me and I left the earth
to escape with you towards the light:
for us the, skies parted their clouds: unknown
splendours, divine glowings half seen …

Alas! alas, sad waking from dreams!
I beg you, O night, to give back to me your illusions:
come back, come back in your radiance:
come back, O mysterious night!

40. Der kranke Mond

Du nächtig todeskranker Mond
Dort auf des Himmels schwarzem Pfühl,
Dein Blick, so fiebernd übergroß,
Bannt mich, wie fremde Melodie.

An unstillbarem Liebesleid
Stirbst du, an Sehnsucht, tief erstickt,
Du nächtig todeskranker Mond,
Dort auf des Himmels schwarzem Pfühl.

Den Liebsten, der im Sinnenrausch
Gedankenlos zur Liebsten geht,
Belustigt deiner Strahlen Spiel –
Dein bleiches, qualgebornes Blut,
Du nächtig todeskranker Mond!

The Ailing Moon

O deathly-sick moon of night,
There on the black couch of heaven,
Your glance, so feverish, wide-eyed,
Holds me spell-bound as by strange melodies

Of the insatiable sorrow of love
You die, of longing, deep and choking.
Oh deathly-sick moon of night,
There on the black couch of heaven.

To the lover – who steals ecstatically,
Heedlessly, to his beloved –
The Play of your beams is gladdening –
Your pale blood, born of torment,
O deathly-sick moon of night.

Albert Giraud trans. Otto Erich Hartleben

World Music

63. Se quema la chumbambá

Candela es, se quema la chumbambá

Mamá que me estoy quemando, Mamá mira que me quemo
En no quemándome yo, que se queme el mundo entero

Que se queme la sabana, se queman los sabaneros
En no quemándome yo, que se queme el mundo entero

Que se queme esta familia, que se queme este tresero,
En no quemándome yo, que se queme el mundo entero

Candela es, se quema la chumbambá
Candela es, se quema y no cuesta na'

Mamá que se queme Emilia, se queman los sabaneros
En no quemándome yo, que se queme el mundo entero

Fire! Our chumbambá[1] is burning

Mama, see how I am afire; look, I am burning
So long as I am not burning, let the whole world blaze

Let the savannah burn; the workers there are burning,
So long as I am not burning, let the whole world blaze

Let the family burn; let the tres[2] player burn,
So long as I am not burning, let the whole world blaze

Fire! Our chumbambá is burning
Fire! It is burning and costs nothing

Mama, let Emilia burn, let the workers in the savannah burn,
So long as I am not burning, let the whole world blaze

[1] a plot of land owned by the singer's family
[2] a guitar with three single or double courses of strings

Copyright acknowledgements

Index

A

A Day in the Life (Lennon & McCartney) 487
Agbekor Dance (Ghana) 532
Après un rêve (Fauré) 363
Armstrong, Louis: *West End Blues* 461
Auric, Georges: *Passport to Pimlico* 369

B

Bach, Johann Sebastian:
    Brandenburg Concerto No. 4 in G 7
    Cantata No. 48, 'Ich elender Mensch' 288
    Partita No. 4 in D, BWV 828 249
Bali: *Baris Melampahan* 522
Baris Melampahan (Bali) 522
Beatles, The: *A Day in the Life* 487
Beethoven, Ludwig van: *Septet in E♭, Op. 20* 207
Berio, Luciano: *Sequenza III for female voice* 171
Berlioz, Hector: *Harold in Italy* 42
Bernstein, Leonard: *On the Waterfront* 374
Black and Tan Fantasy (Duke Ellington) 465
Brahms, Johannes: *Piano Quintet in F minor, Op. 34* 231
Brandenburg Concerto No. 4 in G (J. S. Bach) 7
Bruckner, Anton: *Locus iste* 305

C

Cage, John: *Sonatas and Interludes for Prepared Piano* 166
Cantata No. 48, 'Ich elender Mensch' (J. S. Bach) 288
Concerto for Double String Orchestra (Tippett) 120
Corelli, Arcangelo: *Trio Sonata in D, Op. 3 No. 2* 200
Cuba: *Se quema la chumbambá* 534

D

Davis, Miles: *Four* 468
Debussy, Claude:
    Pour le piano (Sarabande) 260
    Prélude a l'après-midi d'un faune 86
Dekker, Desmond: *You can get it if you really want* 496
Der Doppelgänger (Schubert) 361
'Der kranke Mond' from Pierrot Lunaire (Schoenberg) 364
Dido and Aeneas (Purcell) 356
Don't look back in anger (Oasis) 509
Dowland, John: *Flow my tears* 347

E

Ellington, Duke: *Black and Tan Fantasy* 465
ET (John Williams) 409

F

Fauré, Gabriel : *Après un rêve* 363
Flow my tears (Dowland) 347
Four (Miles Davis) 468

G

Gabrieli, Giovanni:
    In ecclesiis 269
    Sonata pian' e forte 194
Galliard 'Ecce quam bonum' (Holborne) 191
Gershwin, George: *'Summertime' from Porgy and Bess* 366
Ghana: *Agbekor Dance* 532
Gigue: Partita No. 4 in D, BWV 828 (J. S. Bach) 249
Goldsmith, Jerry: *Planet of the Apes* 388

H

Harold in Italy (Berlioz) 42
Haydn, Joseph:
    My mother bids me bind my hair 359
    Nelson Mass 299
    String Quartet in E♭, Op. 33 No. 2, 'The Joke' 202
    Symphony No. 26 in D minor, 'Lamentatione' 31
Holborne, Anthony: *Pavane 'The image of melancholy'*
    and Galliard 'Ecce quam bonum' 191
Honey don't (Carl Perkins) 477
Horner, James: *Titanic* 440
Howlin' Wolf: *I'm leavin' you* 471

I

I'm leavin' you (Howlin' Wolf) 471
'Ich elender Mensch', Cantata No. 48 (J. S. Bach) 288
In ecclesiis (G. Gabrieli) 269
India: *Rag Bhairav* 519
Ireland: *Tom McElvogue's (jig),*
    and New Irish Barndance (reel) 530

J

'Joke, The', String Quartet in E♭, Op. 33 No. 2 (Haydn) 202

K

Kinderscenen, Op. 15 (Schumann) 258
Kinks, The: *Waterloo Sunset* 483
Lamb, The (Tavener) 344

L

'Lamentatione', Symphony No. 26 in D minor (Haydn) 31
Locus iste (Bruckner) 305

M

Monteverdi, Claudio: *Ohimè, se tanto amate* 353
Morse on the Case (Barrington Pheloung) 433
Mozart, Wolfgang Amadeus: *Piano Sonata in B♭, K.333* ... 253
My mother bids me bind my hair (Haydn) 359

N

Nelson Mass (Haydn) 299
New Irish Barndance (reel) 530
New York Counterpoint (Reich) 176

O

O Wilhelme, pastor bone (Taverner) 266
Oasis: *Don't look back in anger* 509
Ohimè, se tanto amate (Monteverdi) 353
On the Waterfront (Bernstein) 374

P

Partita No. 4 in D, BWV 828 (J. S. Bach) 249
Passport to Pimlico (Auric) 369
Pavana Lachrimae (Sweelinck) 245
Pavane 'The image of melancholy' (Holborne) 191
Perkins, Carl: *Honey don't* 477
Pheloung, Barrington: *Morse on the Case* 433
Piano Quintet in F minor, Op. 34 (Brahms) 231
Piano Sonata in B♭, K.333 (Mozart) 253
Pierrot Lunaire: 'Der kranke Mond' (Schoenberg) 364
Planet of the Apes (Jerry Goldsmith) 388
Porgy and Bess (Gershwin) 366
Poulenc, Francis: *Sonata for Horn, Trumpet and Trombone* .. 242
Pour le piano (Debussy) 260
Prélude a l'après-midi d'un faune (Debussy) 86
Prelude and Fugue in A Op. 87 No. 7 (Shostakovich) 262
Prelude to Tristan und Isolde (Wagner) 65
Pulcinella Suite (Stravinsky) 139
Purcell, Henry: *Dido and Aeneas* 356

Q

Quartet Op. 22 (Webern) 160
'Quoniam tu solus' from The Nelson Mass (Haydn) 299

R

Rag Bhairav (India) 519
Reich, Steve: *New York Counterpoint* 176

S

Sarabande: Partita No. 4 in D, BWV 828 (J. S. Bach) 249
Sarabande: Pour le piano (Debussy) 260
Schoenberg, Arnold: *'Der kranke Mond'*
     from Pierrot Lunaire 364
Schubert, Franz: *Der Doppelgänger* 361
Schumann, Robert: *Kinderscenen, Op. 15* 258
Se quema la chumbambá (Cuba) 535
Septet in E♭, Op. 20 (Beethoven) 207
Sequenza III for female voice (Berio) 171
Shostakovich, Dmitry:
     Prelude and Fugue in A Op. 87 No. 7 262
     String Quartet No. 8, Op. 110 163
Sing we at pleasure (Weelkes) 349
Sonata for Horn, Trumpet and Trombone (Poulenc) 242
Sonata pian' e forte (G. Gabrieli) 194
Sonatas and Interludes for Prepared Piano (Cage) 166
Stravinsky, Igor:
     Pulcinella Suite 139
     Symphony of Psalms 307

String Quartet in E♭, Op. 33 No. 2, 'The Joke' (Haydn) 202
String Quartet No. 8, Op. 110 (Shostakovich) 163
'Summertime' from Porgy and Bess (Gershwin) 366
Sweelinck, Jan Pieterszoon: *Pavana Lachrimae* 245
Symphony No. 26 in D minor, 'Lamentatione' (Haydn) 31
Symphony of Psalms (Stravinsky) 307

T

Tavener, John: *The Lamb* 344
Taverner, John: *O Wilhelme, pastor bone* 266
Tippett, Michael: *Concerto for Double String Orchestra* 120
Titanic (James Horner) 440
Tom McElvogue's (jig) (Ireland) 530
Trinidad: *Yellow Bird* 528
Trio Sonata in D, Op. 3 No. 2 (Corelli) 200
Tristan und Isolde: Prelude (Wagner) 65
Tupelo Honey (Van Morrison) 501

V

Van Morrison: *Tupelo Honey* 501

W

Wagner, Richard: *Prelude to Tristan und Isolde* 65
Waterloo Sunset (The Kinks) 483
Webern, Anton: *Quartet Op. 22* 160
Weelkes, Thomas: *Sing we at pleasure* 349
West End Blues (Louis Armstrong) 461
'When I am laid in earth' from Dido and Aeneas (Purcell) ... 356
Williams, John : *ET* 409

Y

Yellow Bird (Trinidad) 528
You can get it if you really want (Desmond Dekker
     and the Aces) 496